A
Harlequin
Romance

OTHER
Harlequin Romances
by MARGARET ROME

Many of these titles are available at your local bookseller,
or through the Harlequin Reader Service.

For a free catalogue listing all available Harlequin Romances,
send your name and address to:

HARLEQUIN READER SERVICE,
M.P.O. Box 707, Niagara Falls, N.Y. 14302
Canadian address: Stratford, Ontario, Canada   N5A 6W4

or use the coupon at the back of this book.

VALLEY
OF PARADISE

by

MARGARET ROME

Harlequin Books

TORONTO • LONDON • NEW YORK • AMSTERDAM • SYDNEY • WINNIPEG

Original hard cover edition published in 1975
by Mills & Boon Limited

SBN 373-01957-2

Harlequin edition published March 1976

Printed in Canada

CHAPTER ONE

WITH trembling fingers Serena smoothed the crumpled newspaper flat to the table. The advertisement that had been the cause of much controversy earlier that afternoon during the office lunch break stared out in bold black print. The office junior had drawn their attention to it. Pop-eyed with excitement, she had cut through the general conversation with a scream that had splattered crumbs all over her senior colleagues.

'*Wow*, look at this!' she had spluttered. 'This could be a real gas – a real rave-up . . .!'

With a shudder of disgust Paula Vickers had brushed a crumb from her lambswool sweater. 'You disgusting little beast!' she had rebuked sharply. 'Must we put up with this kind of behaviour every time you see a pop concert advertised?'

'Pop concert be blowed!' young Joy had answered. 'Look for yourself – although as you're not a blue-eyed blonde you needn't feel free to apply.'

'Apply for what?' Paula had eyed her coldly.

'For this job!' Joy had sighed heavy exasperation. 'You never listen, Paula! Anyway, your disposition is all wrong too, so you wouldn't be interested.'

By then the rest of the girls had been agog with

curiosity. 'What *are* you on about?' they had chorused.

'Shan't tell you!' Joy had decided to tease, then quickly changed her mind when the girls had begun advancing in a manner holding decided threat. 'All right, see for yourselves,' she had capitulated, thrusting the paper into an outstretched hand.

Slowly, incredulously, the advertisement had been read out aloud. 'English girl required for post demanding absolute and total commitment in return for lifelong security and freedom from want. Must be of discreet, docile disposition and of fair complexion. Dependants welcome. Telephone following number for appointment.'

After an amazed silence the girls had dissolved into laughter. 'No girl in this day and age would fall for a gag like that!' one of them had howled. 'The advertiser, whoever he is, must be out of his mind!'

'Either that, or he's rich and arrogant enough to think money can buy flesh and blood,' Paula had offered. 'My guess is he's an Arab sheik looking for a new plaything for his harem!'

'Oh, it's just got to be a hoax!' a second girl had opined. 'Even Arab sheiks must be aware that the naïve sort of girl likely to fall for that line simply doesn't exist these days, and especially not here in London!'

Laughter had been at its height when Joy, staring thoughtfully in Serena's direction, had offered slowly, 'Oh, I dunno ... Serena might fit the bill ...'

Deeply preoccupied, Serena had been only vaguely aware of the conversation eddying around her. Her mind had been buzzing with the problem of how much longer she was going to be able to afford the exorbitant fees demanded by the day nursery. Earlier that morning while she was depositing baby Wendy as usual, the nursery supervisor had been very apologetic. 'I'm sorry, Miss Payne, but as from next week we're having to up our charges by an extra pound.' Avoiding Serena's shocked expression, she had turned away, mumbling, 'It's to do with inflation, you know ... difficult, but unavoidable ...'

For the rest of the day Serena's mind had wrestled with the problem of how she was to find the extra pound. Already she was skimping on meals to such an extent that remarks were being made about her look of fragility, and her feeble excuse of having to diet had been greeted with scorn from girls who envied her natural slenderness.

Then suddenly she had become aware of a battery of eyes and a void of silence during which everyone seemed to be expecting her to comment.

'What ... what did you say? I'm sorry, I wasn't listening ...'

Only Paula had answered, but in such an oblique way that Serena had remained puzzled. With an exasperated shrug she had commented, 'Perhaps on this occasion you may be right, Joy. Only last week, or so I've been told, Serena accepted an invitation from the office wolf to visit his flat to listen to his collection of classical records.'

Serena had blushed a furious red. 'Well, why not? It was a most enjoyable evening and I thought it was very kind of Mr. Jason to ask me.'

'And so it would have been, my dear,' Paula had replied dryly, 'if kindness had motivated the invitation. I don't know how you managed to come out of his flat unscathed, but obviously you did because the following morning he was heard to say that the operation had been a washout so far as he was concerned. He even went so far as to admit that for the first time in his life he had been bothered by scruples and that not even he, and I quote: "was knave enough to prematurely awaken a sleeping beauty".'

'I wonder what he meant . . .?' Serena had puzzled. The laughter that had followed had not been unkind, but even so she had felt humiliated and somehow soiled. As they had returned to their desks to resume work, one of the older women had delayed long enough to murmur,

'Don't distress yourself, my dear. Sophistication is a skin that covers many blemishes. Naïve you may be, but your strength is the strength of ten because your heart is pure.'

Curiosity had prompted Serena to stuff the discarded newspaper into her handbag, and now, as she stared down at the advertisement, the gist of the puzzling conversation became humiliatingly obvious.

Then everything was forgotten when Wendy began to cry, a small whimpering sound Serena knew only too well would develop into a furious scream if she were not immediately consoled. The little mite was teething and every night for weeks pain had given rise to bouts of crying which no amount of petting seemed to ease. Hastily she lifted Wendy from her cot and held her against her shoulder, whispering soft words of comfort into the tiny ear. 'There, there, my sweet, don't cry, please don't cry. You know how annoyed our nasty landlady gets when you disturb the other tenants.' She brushed the hot little face with her cool cheek wondering, not for the first time, if her problems would ever cease.

Slowly she paced the small bedsitter, rocking the tense little body in her arms in an attempt to quieten the child's hysterical sobbing. To her relief the sobs died down, and as she continued pacing, terrified in case it should resume, Serena's thoughts slipped back in time to just over a year ago when life had been so happy, so full of joy, love and promise. It was a painful resurrection, but memories were all she had left of the mother and father whose happiness at the thought of becoming parents once again after a lapse of nineteen years had been tempered slightly by the embarrassment of having to inform their grown-up daughter of the coming event. They had been nervous, uncertain of her reaction, and their joy had been made all the greater by Serena's rapturous reception of their news.

They had mentioned it one evening after supper. Her mother had waited until they were all settled comfortably in the lounge of the small bungalow attached to the filling station owned by her father.

'Serena darling,' she had began, blushing like a teenager, 'your father and I have some wonderful news.'

'Oh, yes?' Absently she had answered, continuing to scan the situations vacant column in the local newspaper. Only a week previously she had graduated from secretarial college and the most important issue on her horizon at that moment had been the finding of an interesting job.

'Please put down that paper and listen, dear,' her mother had urged. Serena had looked up and at the sight of her father's expression of boyish excitement she had slowly laid down the paper and given them both her undivided attention.

'Your father has something to tell you,' her mother had proceeded.

'No, you tell her,' he had insisted.

'No, you ...'

'Oh, for heaven's sake!' Serena had jumped to her feet and held out a hand to each. 'Why don't you both tell me?'

And they had. Simultaneously, with pride

reflecting in their shining eyes, they had burst out:
'We're going to have a baby!'

For a stunned second she had stared at her
parents as if they were beings from another planet,
unable to equate them with such an event, unable to
accept that the happy, closely-knit trio was about to
be made into a quartet. Her first impulse had been
to rebel against the notion, but when anxiety had
clouded their faces she had felt ashamed of her
selfishness and had immediately reassured them.

'Darlings, that's wonderful news! I've always
longed to have a brother or sister, it doesn't matter
which!'

Her mother had almost cried with relief and after
sending her a grateful glance her father had enfolded his wife into his arms and chided gently,
'There now, didn't I tell you she would be as delighted as we are?' But during the months following
joy had become tinged with worry as the date of the
birth approached. Their family doctor had become
a more and more frequent visitor until reluctantly
he had confessed himself worried about the state of
his patient's health. They ought to have been prepared for the final dreadful outcome, but no one
could have connected death with Ann Payne's
happy, laughing face that had refused to acknowl-
edge defeat even when pain was at its most severe.

When the blow had finally fallen Serena and her
father had been totally shattered. For hours they
had waited in a hospital ante-room near to the ward

where the person they loved most in the world was fighting for her own life and for the life of her child. The ashtrays had been piled high with her father's half-smoked cigarettes and the table littered with untouched cups of tea when finally a grey-faced doctor had walked in to inform them sadly,

'I'm sorry, Mr. Payne – Miss Payne, we did all we could, but . . . If it's any consolation, we did manage to save the child.'

From that moment Serena had never managed to erase from her mind the picture of her father's ravaged face, and for weeks after the funeral he had walked about in a state of numbness, speaking only when forced to and then in an abstract, dazed manner that convinced her he had heard nothing of what she had said and cared even less. When, a few months later, a sympathetic policeman had broken the news that her father had been involved in a fatal motor accident she had wept but had not grieved for the man whose heart had been buried with his beloved wife. Indeed, she had had no time to grieve. The demands of her infant sister had been so great they left her no time for solitary thought or for feelings of despair which in different circumstances might have caused her collapse.

The problems had been pressing and plentiful. Both the bungalow and filling station were mortgaged and had to be sold, leaving her a residue sufficient only to cover immediate expenses during the time she spent searching for a bedsitter within easy reach of the job she took simply because the office was in close proximity to the day nursery which, by a stroke of good fortune, was willing and able to accommodate baby Wendy.

Gently Serena eased the sleeping child back into her cot. There were sums to be done, somehow or other she had to squeeze another pound out of her already stretched budget. She drew a chair up to the table and with pencil poised wrote a list of all necessary expenditure. Already she had cut out hairdos, shoe repairs and cosmetics. Luckily, her hair reacted well to a home shampoo and with the help of an expert trim every two weeks the heavy golden waves remained reasonably well groomed.

Tights were an expensive item. Perhaps if she bought a heavier gauge and was careful to avoid that part of her desk with the rough splinters she might manage to make them last longer than a week! The soup and rolls she had at lunchtime were a must if she were to keep at bay the alarming dizzy spells she was perfectly well aware were caused by lack of substantial meals.

Thoughtfully she glanced across at the sleeping infant, noting with satisfaction the well-rounded cheeks and sturdy little limbs. Perhaps Wendy would not miss the odd bar of chocolate she had been in the habit of buying? Yet all babies needed to be spoiled a little and it was such a small extravagance. Reluctantly, knowing she had to be severe, she scored a heavy pencil line through the word chocolate on her list. But even with tights and chocolate removed she was still fifty pence short of her target.

Worry lines furrowed her brow as she chewed the end of her pencil. A whimper from the cot went unnoticed and a few seconds later the room resounded to a wail of baby anger that startled Serena to her feet.

'Oh, no, not again!' She lifted Wendy from her cot, but the child was inconsolable and ten long minutes dragged past before her piercing cries became reduced to a pained whimper.

Serena was tentatively lowering her back into the cot when a thunderous rapping on the door startled the baby out of her half-slumber. As her howling recommenced Serena glanced desperately from the cot to the door, wondering which exercise should take priority. Deciding Wendy could not be abandoned, she hurried across to open the door with the child still in her arms and found an irate landlady glowering on the threshold. Flushed and dishevelled, Serena began stuttering an apology.

'I'm sorry, Mrs. Collins—'

'So am I, Miss Payne,' the grim-faced woman cut in. 'Sorry to have to tell you that you must vacate this room within a week. I've been very patient, but Mr. Gent next door is threatening to leave because of the disturbance caused by the child's crying. I'm sorry, but I'm listening to no more excuses, I want to re-let this room next Saturday!'

She stalked off, leaving Serena speechless with despair. Slowly she closed the door, hugging close the baby who, ironically, was now sleeping peacefully. She stared down at the innocent face until tears blurred her vision, then hastily she placed her in her cot, sat down at the table and buried her aching head in her outstretched arms.

For half an hour she sobbed, giving rein to the hopelessness and despair that had dogged her for the past year. She had reached the absolute end of her tether; fate seemed determined to deal her one blow after another, bludgeoning her with worries in an attempt to break the spirit that had kept her struggling valiantly when others would have given in. But now she had to admit defeat. Once, Paula had suggested she put the baby in a home and the idea had horrified her, but now she had to force herself to consider the possibility, even though every sensitive nerve shrank from such action.

She tried to marshal her thoughts in that direction, but even to think of taking such a step caused her a wave of faintness. Slowly she raised her head, her red-rimmed eyes travelling slowly around the sparsely furnished room. Threadbare carpets, one rickety armchair, a bed, a sink under which a gas meter poked its ugly head. A dreadfully bare, badly heated little room, yet to Wendy and herself it represented security and togetherness. Anything would be preferable to separation from the mite who was all she had left of the family she had so dearly loved.

Her lacklustre eyes fell upon the newspaper left outspread upon the table. Listlessly she pulled it forward, scanning the printed words without interest until once again her attention was captured by the advertisement couched in such enigmatic terms. One sentence stood out from the rest. Two words that dropped like manna from heaven before her despairing eyes.

Dependants welcome!

She did not stop to think. Feverishly she tore the strip of paper containing the telephone number from the printed page and dashed down the stairs to the communal telephone in the hallway. She made three attempts before her shaking fingers dialled the correct digits and when a voice answered she stuttered out her request for an interview with the unknown advertiser.

Tersely, a time and place were given before the call was abruptly terminated.

She stared down at the piece of paper upon which she had scribbled the given instructions.

Saturday. 2.30 p.m. Imperial Hotel. Room 1005.

That was tomorrow! What a blessing she had been given so little time in which to change her mind!

CHAPTER TWO

WHAT to wear for the interview presented no problem. Her one decent outfit comprised a skirt and jacket in a shade of brown that contrasted suitably demure against the blazing glory of her shoulder-length hair. A cream-coloured blouse, neat brown shoes and a matching shoulder bag completed the outfit which, when she stared into her mirror, seemed to Serena to reflect unexcitingly drably. She frowned. If the girls were right and her prospective employer was an Arab sheik there was little chance that he would give her a second glance.

Her heart began to race. She had forced herself not to think of the possible dire consequences to herself but had dwelt only upon the one great advantage that might accrue from her impulsive action.

Dependants welcome, the advertisement had said, so if he were a man of his word and if she got the job then Wendy's future wellbeing would be assured. A quick glance at her watch told her that she had less than ten minutes in which to reach the hotel. Wendy was being cared for by a sympathetic neighbour and the taxi she had ordered was due to arrive any minute, so she grabbed her handbag, cast a last despairing look into the mirror, then hurried outside to face what could be either deliverance or disaster.

The taxi deposited her at the front of the Imperial Hotel with minutes to spare. In a breathless tremble she requested the receptionist to advise her anonymous advertiser that she was waiting to be interviewed and for five painful minutes suffered the inquisitive, covert glances of hotel staff who were, she realized with a blush, bound to be aware of the situation and were probably agog to examine any applicant brave or foolish enough to answer such a curiously worded advertisement.

Her relief was tremendous when a page-boy approached with a request that she should follow him into the lift. Her shaking legs would barely carry her across the width of luxurius carpet and when the lift doors slid together with smooth, noiseless precision she felt she was being whisked away from the world of sanity towards an alien planet. No one in her world would attempt to buy a human being, for that was what the advertisement had implied. Absolute, total commitment, it had said, in return for lifelong security. Bondage, in other words. A prison with silken bars and cushioned cells in return for *what?* Panic fluttered in her throat like the beating of a thousand frenzied wings. She struggled to voice a request to the boy to stop the lift and take her back to her own familiar world, but just then the lift stopped and the boy swung open the gates and stepped out into a passageway, indicating that she should follow him.

Deep blue carpet muffled their footsteps as they travelled the length of the passageway and stopped outside of a door bearing the numbers 1005.

'Th ... thank you,' she stammered, fumbling inside of her purse for a small coin. But with an engaging wink he refused the proffered tip and set off back towards the lift. Seconds later he was gone, leaving her stranded outside the door which might well open up a completely new life. Her hand fluttered upwards to knock upon the door panel, then hesitated and slid back down to her side. She had not the nerve to go through with it! Tales she had heard of white slave traffic flashed across her mind, tales of girls who had answered similar advertisements only to end up in some dingy area of Port Said entertaining Arab sheiks for innumerable hours a day and very little pay.

'You're a *fool*, Serena Payne!' she muttered as she dithered at the doorway. 'There's bound to be a better way out than this, after all, departments have been set up solely to help people in your predicament. These are the days of the welfare state, no one need go hungry or be without a roof over her head!' Then in her mind's eyes she saw a picture of Wendy becoming institutionalized, her individuality swamped by the demands of dozens of other destitute children, and it was all the spur she needed to urge her on.

Almost as soon as her knuckles descended upon the panel the door was opened by an urbane manservant who looked her over without a flicker of interest as he stepped aside, mutely inviting her to enter. The room was so sumptuously furnished it took her breath away. It was sacrilegious even to think of treading the area of off-white carpet flowing under elegantly-curved legs of tables and chairs, finally ending up lapping pale blue skirting protecting walls hung with gilt-framed mirrors and delicate colour prints whose pastel shades offered relief to the stark simplicity of white walls. Although the sun was shining through large-paned windows, a fire crackling in the hearth was a surprising find amid the modern, centrally-heated surroundings.

She stumbled to a halt, wavering uncertainly behind a high-backed chair while the manservant bent to inform its occupant of her presence. She tensed, not knowing what to expect, and was immediately relieved when a tall, elderly gentleman stood up and turned to receive her.

'Miss Payne?' His beautifully modulated voice was slightly accented. French, she thought at first, then changed her mind when, with old-world dignity, he inquired, 'Would the *señorita* care to take a seat?'

As she obeyed her wide eyes roved his lean, aristocratic features. The eyes were piercing and showed slight surprise, but the clean-cut mouth was kind. In his youth the snow-white hair would have been black, she decided, the eyes daring and mouth audacious, but the long, lean body just as slim. She waited for him to speak, her fears ebbing as she noted his struggle to find words. She sensed that the experience was new to the assured old gentleman and her mouth took on an encouraging, sympathetic curve as she waited until he regained his composure.

'First of all let me introduce myself, *señorita*. I am El Conde Alberto de Valdivia, and your name, I believe, is Serena?'

'Yes, Señor Conde . . .' she stumbled.

A lean hand waved dissent. 'Don Alberto will suffice, my dear. I expressed my full title purely in your own interest – in case you should wish to check up on me once the purpose of your visit has been made known.'

'Thank you, Don Alberto,' she whispered nervously, 'but I wouldn't dream of checking up on you.'

'And why not?' His brows beetled. 'You know nothing of me except that I have advertised for an English girl, an advertisement worded in such a manner that any normal person reading it must immediately have suffered misgivings. Am I not right?'

She nodded. 'I do have a few questions I would like answered.'

'I will answer as many questions as you wish,' he agreed, 'but first of all we will have some of your English tea.' He pressed a bell and when his manservant appeared requested, 'Tea for the English miss, Pedro, and for once I feel inclined to share in this very civilized ritual.'

She sensed that the man was surprised, although his expression did not alter as he bowed before making his exit. When the door closed behind him Don Alberto's attention was turned upon Serena. His dark eyes reflected approval of all he saw as curiously he examined her from the toes of her neat brown shoes to the tip of her head which, bathed in shafts of sunlight, had taken on a molten glow.

'Tell me, *señorita,* which facet of my advertisement appealed to you most? Was it the promise of lifelong security, perhaps, or freedom from money worries?' Cynically, his lips twisted. 'In the past few days many young English women have sat opposite me in that very same chair. All were blonde, all professed to be discreet and of docile temperament, and each without exception confessed to having been attracted by the promise of luxury and wealth. However, I feel some of the virtues they claimed were as false as was the colour of their hair. I may be old and a little out of touch, but even I know the difference between natural gold and that which is obtained from a bottle.'

'My hair is not dyed, *señor,*' her chin tilted. 'And I have no desire for wealth or luxury for myself.'

'Ah!' he drawled meaningfully. 'Then for whom, may I ask?'

'Your advertisement,' she stumbled on, 'stated that dependants would be welcome. I have a baby —

she's a year old, and because she's teething and has been crying rather a lot my landlady has told me that I must find other accommodation. Added to that, the nursery where Wendy stays while I'm at work has upped its charges and I'm terribly afraid that I won't be able to stretch my salary to meet the new rate. That's why I answered your advertisement – I'm desperate for somewhere to live where Wendy and I can be together. If I can't find such a place the baby may be taken away from me and put in a home. I'll do anything to avoid that, anything!'

She dragged her eyes from her lap and looked up at the man whose expression had changed from indulgence to deep distaste. Taut fingers caressed his outthrust chin as he frowningly considered.

'I thought my quest had ended,' he muttered. 'When you walked through the door looking so sweetly innocent I felt sure you were the one. But a child ...! Ah, me.' he sighed, 'the morals of today's generation are truly beyond me.'

She jumped to her feet, her cheeks aflame with indignation. 'Wendy is not *my* baby, she's my sister, my baby sister! How could you think ...'

Don Alberto's face did not lighten. Sadly he shook his head. 'My dear, it is only to be expected that you should make excuses.'

'I'm making *no* excuses!' She stamped her foot, timidity forgotten in the face of such an outrageous supposition. Barely able to keep her voice steady, she

23

spelled out, 'I was nineteen when my mother was told to expect another addition to the family. Because of her age ... complications, I'm not sure exactly what ... she died when Wendy was born, then a few months later my father was killed in a road accident. Since then I've looked after Wendy as best I could, but as I'm still not earning a very high salary it's been hard, sometimes impossible, to make ends meet. That's the reason I'm here. Your advertisement seemed to offer a new life for Wendy and myself. I don't want luxury, neither do I want money, but I do desperately need some place where I can bring up my sister without the continual worry of finding someone to look after her while I'm at work and where she can live the life of a normal happy child without having to be shushed quiet and having all her natural youthful spirit suppressed. That's all I wanted, *señor*, that's all I shall ever want! Good day—' She pulled on her gloves, close to tears. 'Don't bother to ring for your manservant, I'll find my own way out.'

With surprising agility the old gentleman jumped to his feet. 'Please don't go, *señorita*. I apologize, obviously I have misjudged you. Won't you please stay and listen to what I have to say?'

The temptation to sweep out of the room was baulked by the arrival of Pedro wheeling in a laden trolley. 'Please,' Don Alberto coaxed, 'stay and pour out for me.'

His charm was impossible to resist and after a few

seconds' wavering she succumbed. 'Very well, *señor*, I accept your apology; I will stay and have tea with you.'

She did not know why she should be suddenly reminded of a satisfied puma preening in his lair. Perhaps it was the purr in his voice when he begged her to be seated, or it might have been the glow in dark eyes that followed every delicate movement as she poured pale amber tea into transparent china cups. As they helped themselves to wafer-thin sandwiches and sipped the refreshing liquid he probed further, eliciting every detail of her past life without her being aware that she was being thoroughly questioned. A third degree, so skilfully carried out that she felt nothing but gratitude for his interest. His charm was such that she became completely relaxed. It was as if she were in the company of a favourite uncle, one who was interested, one who cared so much about her wellbeing he was happy to remain silent while she poured into his receptive ears all the fears and disappointments of the past and her hopes for the future.

She was amazed when a clock chiming the hour of four cut across their amiable conversation. 'Goodness, it can't be that time already! I told my neighbour I'd be gone only an hour, I really must go!'

Don Alberto looked startled. 'But we have much to talk about yet, little one. You have not yet heard the details of the position I am about to offer you!'

'You mean ... you intend offering me the job?' she breathed.

'You and no other,' he smiled, gesturing her back to her chair, 'though, of course, the final decision must be yours.' Sensitive to the gravity of his manner, she sank back into her seat and waited expectantly. 'You have heard of Chile?' he asked so abruptly that she was startled.

'Not much. It's in South America, isn't it?'

He nodded. 'That is correct, a bean-shaped republic sandwiched between the towering Andes mountains and the Pacific Ocean. Along the southwest coast of America, Chile sits between snow-topped peaks and white-capped waves. My homeland is beautiful, a land where you need not hesitate to take your baby sister, a long, narrow corridor of land in which nature displays different climates and landscapes. To the north is the sun-scorched deserts where it has not rained for ten years or more, and in the south forests where people joke that it rains three hundred and sixty-six days in the year. Glaciers feed the rushing streams, the rivers and deep blue lakes, and between the desert and the ice lies the central valley, the long fertile plain in which my home is situated. The climate is good, summers cool and dry, winters mild and rainy.

'My family first settled there in the sixteenth century; they were *conquistadors*, Spanish adventurers who set out to explore the new land and to search for gold. They found no gold, but they did find deep happiness and contentment in the land where they finally decided to settle and rear their families. It was not easy at first, hostile Indians had to be subdued and many lives were lost during those early years, but now the families of the original Spanish settlers consider themselves more Chilean than Spanish. We are proud of the Indians' courage and love of freedom and believe that their spirit, together with our own Spanish traditions, has shaped the history of our country. Chile is no longer a Spanish dominion, of course, but is a young republic cut off from the rest of the world by mountains, desert and sea. Wars and rebellions have torn us apart. Violent earthquakes have shattered our cities and tidal waves have drowned our coastal towns – and still do. Whole towns have vanished, mountains have tumbled, dead volcanoes have burst into fiery life and new ones pushed skyward overnight. A young country, turbulent, unpredictable and as impulsive as the young *huasos* whom I employ on my *hacienda* to keep watch over my herds of cattle.'

'*Huasos?*' Serena echoed, awestricken.

'*Vaquero ... gaucho ...* How do you say cowboy,' he twinkled, then sobered suddenly. 'My grandson is such a one. In years to come he will, of course, take over from me the running of the *hacienda*, but at present he is living the life of a *huaso* and will continue to do so until I feel the time is ripe for me to hand over to him his inheritance. It is on his behalf that I am here in this country, it was on his behalf that I inserted the advertisement, and it is on his behalf that I want you to travel with me to the other side of the world to become his bride!'

She could not have been more startled had he bared vicious teeth. 'Wh . . . *what*?'

Sombrely, he returned her horrified stare. 'Yes, my dear, that is the nature of the position you are being offered. My grandson needs a wife and I consider myself the only one capable of judging the kind of woman to whom a man of his calibre would be best suited. I am old, *señorita*,' he murmured on a tired breath, 'and my dearest wish is to relinquish the running of the *hacienda* into responsible hands. As a married man my grandson will be better able to command the respect of the older men with whom we do business and also the younger of our employees, who have been encouraged to regard him as one of themselves, will become more quickly adapted to his new authority.'

Selina gasped, her head spinning, trying to cope with the breathtaking vista opened up by the Señor's words. Snow-topped peaks, white-capped waves, sun-scorched deserts and rain-soaked forests where audacious *conquistadors* had fought savage Indians hampering their quest for gold! The violent earthquakes he had mentioned could have caused no less upheaval than that which his outrageous suggestion of marriage had caused to her youthful, timid spirit. Turbulent, unpredictable young cowboys were far removed from her way of life, as insubstantial as images cast upon celluloid screens which were all her imagination had to draw upon. Seated comfortably inside a cinema, she could enjoy watching herds of cattle being driven across miles of rangeland, could admire the horsemanship and skill of the riders who, after spending days and nights in the saddle, then erupted into some nearby town in search of robust, tempestuous relaxation. Steaks roasting over an open fire were a mythical joy to the girl whose most substantial meal of late had consisted of scrambled egg or baked beans, but the most astonishing aspect of all was that of being asked to become the wife of one of those alien beings.

Her bemused eyes reflected shock as they dwelt upon the face of the elderly gentleman. 'Are you serious?' she croaked.

Arrogantly distended nostrils betrayed his distaste of the question. 'I do not joke, *señorita*,' was his stiff reply.

'But your grandson,' she gasped, 'how does he feel about such an arrangement? What kind of a man would allow his grandfather to choose his bride?'

'What kind of man?' Don Alberto mused. 'In many ways he is very like his father, my only son, who to my bitter regret lost his life in one of the earthquakes I mentioned previously. He and his wife had gone into town for a short break, leaving their son in my charge. It was to have been a light-hearted shopping spree, one of the many ways in which my son indulged the wife he adored – deservedly so, because she was beautiful and loving and they were ideally happy together. They both died when the hotel in which they were staying disappeared into a fissure opened up by the 'quake. My grandson was too young to retain any memory of his parents, but each day I see in him some reminder of his father who, in the latter years of his young life, bestowed upon me such pride and happiness as I had never known before nor have known since. Only a few weeks before his death he thanked me for my guidance and advice and in just the same way I hope my grandson will also thank me for setting him upon the course of true fulfilment. As to how he will react . . .' a veil was drawn across his eyes, leaving them coldly expressionless, 'he will, of course, do whatever I say.'

Serena felt a sudden stab of pity for the man who for years had stood in the shadow of his imperious grandfather. Brought up as he had been from birth by such a *grande hidalgo*, his shy inability to find a wife for himself was understandable. He must necessarily have grown up lacking self-assurance, probably to the point of developing a large inferiority complex, a shy, introverted character, she imagined, sensitive to criticism and very much lacking confidence in his own judgment.

Nevertheless, however much sympathy she felt towards the unfortunate man, marriage to him was out of the question!

She told Don Alberto quietly and with dignity,

'I'm sorry, but you must look elsewhere for a wife for your grandson.'

'Why?' he rapped. 'Are you already in love with some man?'

'No, it's not that,' she assured him.

'Then why do you lie? A short while ago you professed yourself willing to do anything to obtain a home for your sister. What I have offered is a little better than *anything*, indeed some might consider you extremely fortunate to be given the chance of exchanging the life you now lead for the one I have outlined.'

'But don't you see?' she protested. 'It's absolutely out of the question for me to marry a man I've never met, a man I haven't even seen!'

'But you do wish to marry!' he pounced.

'Well, yes,' colour stampeded into her cheeks, 'some day I hope . . . I expect . . .'

Smooth as silk, he interrupted, 'Perhaps you expect too much, *señorita*. Ask yourself, what man would wish to shoulder the burden of a child that is not his own? Man is a selfish creature; not even for love will he reject his own comforts. I can picture you in years to come, old before your time due to the strain of bringing up a child alone; left to struggle on unaided during her schooldays, then later, when she grows up and falls in love, left again to a lonely old age, unloved, unwanted and – unless the child turns out to be exceptional – selfishly unrewarded.'

Serena gasped, 'You are cruel, *señor*!'

'Realistic, *señorita*, and you would do well to follow my example.'

He turned on his heel and strode out of the room, leaving her to consider his words. Within the warmth of the overheated room she shivered, touched by fear – fear of loneliness, fear of old age, fear of the unwanted state he had declared would be her fate. Automatically she reached for a sandwich, then discarded it with a shudder, disgusted by the squirrel instinct that had urged her to store up food as an insurance against leaner days. She glanced around the elegantly appointed room, comparing it with the sordid place that was to remain their home for less than a week. After next Saturday – what then? Where would they go, how would they fare, and how much longer could she continue the hand-to-mouth existence which, when Wendy grew old enough to understand, would be bound to form the basis of an insecurity that might hamper her for the rest of her life.

When Don Alberto re-entered the room she was gazing composedly into the heart of the fire. She looked up when he approached and a faint smile in her eyes encouraged him to ask, 'You have decided, *señorita*?'

'Yes, *señor*,' she replied simply. 'I have decided to accept the proposal you extended on behalf of your grandson; I shall try to make him an acceptable wife.'

CHAPTER THREE

THREE days later Serena stood gazing down out of the window of a skyscraper hotel upon a plaza below where a squad of *carabiñeros* were marching briskly to the beat of a military band. It was the changing of the guard around the Casa de la Moneda, the Chilean 'White House' and home of the president. The guard wore peaked caps, khaki uniforms with trousers tucked into knee-high black leather boots and as they lined up facing the soldiers about to be relieved, officers drew swords and saluted each other with swift, skilful gestures. Two by two, the guards changed places until the new group had completely switched positions with the old, then the band struck up a martial tune and the *carabiñeros* set off marching through the streets of Santiago, back to their barracks. The whole of the capital was spread out before her, built on a broad plain, a river cut through the northern section, while to the east lay a gigantic, jagged line of rocks, earth and snow – the Andes mountains.

Less than twenty-four hours ago they had still been in London. Wendy had behaved beautifully during the flight, playing up to Don Alberto's delighted attentions in the manner of a born coquette. Cradled in Serena's arms, she had fastened her great blue eyes upon his face, wooing him with gurgles of affection and wide smiles that had uncovered the first tender shoots of glistening milk teeth. So entranced had the man become that he had finally insisted upon nursing her, leaving Serena free to examine her thoughts, to wonder at her wild folly, to speculate upon the gossip her absence from the office was bound to have caused.

The speed with which all the arrangements had been accomplished had left her gasping. Don Alberto's manservant had seen to everything except the termination of her employment. That she had managed to do herself with one telephone call.

'Owing to domestic circumstances I have been forced to find other lodgings,' she had squirmed as she misled her sympathetic boss. 'As my new place is quite some distance from the office, would you be so kind as to waive my week's notice in order that I might accept a job I have been offered near to my new digs?'

'Certainly, my dear,' her boss had agreed affably. 'We'll be sorry to lose you, but as the office is going through a slack period at present your abrupt departure will not cause too much of an upset. Call in whenever it's convenient to collect your holiday money and insurance cards.'

She had called at a time when she knew most of the girls would be out to lunch, deliberately avoiding poignant farewells and curious questions she was too cowardly to answer. She could number no special friends amongst her office colleagues, they had all been kind, but of necessity she had had to refuse invitations to join in social activities after office hours because Wendy had taken up all of her free time. She would be talked about for a couple of days, then forgotten, she reflected ruefully, a ship that had passed in the night, a nondescript person who had made little or no impact upon their lives.

She sighed and moved away from the window towards the bed. Upon their arrival at the hotel Wendy had been whisked out of her arms by a capable woman assigned by the manager as nurse-maid for the duration of their short stay.

'Sleep for a few hours, if you can, my dear,' Don Alberto had urged, 'then meet me downstairs for lunch. We have much to discuss in the short time left to us before setting out for the *hacienda*.'

She felt glad to obey, so much had happened in such a short time she was feeling bewildered, lost and frightened by the sights and sounds of this strange, unfamiliar country. She stretched out on the bed, but her tiredness was more mental than physical and not even the cradling comfort of a luxurious mattress or the caress of silken covers could ease the torment of an overworked mind. She was engaged by proxy to a man she had never met! Would she be strong enough support for this shy individual who was to become her husband? Could mutual need serve as a substitute for love during a lifetime of marriage? She stirred restlessly, weariness

35

overpowering thought. As heavy lashes wavered over drowsy eyes her mind began drifting into forbidden channels. A dream she had sworn to relinquish found release against her weakened defences, a dream she had cherished inwardly over the past year, a fantasy wherein a man strong as tempered steel, immovable as rock, indomitable of will, swept into her life to shoulder all her burdens, restore happiness to her aching heart, revive her flagging spirits and with arrogant charm arouse within her a flaming torch of love . . .

Tears were still clinging to her lashes when she awoke an hour later. A quick glance at her watch told her that she had an hour to spare before the appointed lunch time. Midday sun was streaming through half-closed shutters which she herself had thrown wide open just before lying down to rest. Drowsily curious, she looked around, suspecting an alien presence, but the room was deserted. Whoever it was who had closed the shutters must have crept around noiselessly so as not to disturb her sleep. Feeling uncomfortably spied upon, she hastened across the room to belatedly turn the key in the lock of her bedroom door. It was foolish of her, she knew, but her sense of vulnerability was such that even the click of a lock brought a small measure of comfort.

Deciding to take a shower, she turned towards the bathroom, then stopped suddenly, her progress barred by a pile of cardboard boxes, grey in colour, of all sizes and shapes, each emblazoned with a scrawled signature embossed in gold. 'Mirabelle,' she spelled out slowly, reaching for the topmost box and shaking it carefully. A rustle of tissue paper excited her interest, so tentatively she probed open the lid, uncovering swathes of pale mauve tissue paper that whispered exciting noises at the touch of her trembling fingers. Beneath its folds she caught a glimpse of lace, then the shimmer of silk, before finally she lifted from its pale mauve nest a negligée so lovely that she cried out with sheer pleasure.

She tried the next box, then the next, becoming more and more overawed as each yielded articles more breathtaking than the last. Dresses, underwear, evening gowns, smartly tailored slacks, eye-catching suits, all with matching bags and shoes, each item shrieking of fabulous expense. She was knee-deep in tissue paper by the time she came to the last box, a deeper, broader box she could hardly wait to open. Its contents brought a gasp of amazed incredulity when she whisked away the last fold of tissue paper and uncovered a coat of dark lustrous fur that rippled voluptuously under the stroke of her hesitant fingers.

She sank to her knees and gazed with disbelief at the surrounding array of wealth. No film star could have had a more opulent wardrobe, and the cost . . .! Her frugal instincts winced from putting a price upon such a flood of extravagance.

Being young and feminine she lost no time in

showering and slipping into a set of diaphanous underwear before deciding which outfit to wear for her meeting with her wealthy benefactor. After much deliberation she chose a simple white dress of *broderie anglaise*, its scooped-out neckline slotted through with ribbon of pale blue. She found, upon looking into a mirror, that simplicity was a blind. Expert cutting and clever tailoring had resulted in a creation which, while sheathing her curves in demureness, lent provocation to outthrust breasts and turned her lissom young body into a trap for the eyes of unwary males.

Not even cosmetics had been forgotten, and as she applied pale, pink lipstick to her tremulous mouth and brushed blue shadow across her lids she found time to reflect upon the kind of man who knew so well how to please and excite even the most unsophisticated of her sex. Intuitive as the devil, no doubt of that, penetrating to a degree, with eyes that had seen behind her couldn't-care-less attitude towards feminine fripperies and had gauged her taste to perfection, assessing so thoroughly that he even knew the size of her shoes!

After a quick look to make sure Wendy was sleeping peacefully, Serena tripped light as air downstairs to the bar where she had arranged to meet the Señor for a pre-lunch aperitif. He was seated at a table by the window, but rose to his feet immediately she entered. A surge of gratitude impelled her to reach out a hand towards him and to her surprise he lifted it to his lips, murmuring appreciatively after brushing aside her thanks,

'*El fuego hermoso.*' Translating for her benefit, 'The beautiful flame.'

Sunlight pouring through a window struck living fire from the heavy braids of hair entwined around her youthful head as she nodded acknowledgment of the compliment.

'*Gracias, señor,* I felt I had to do justice to my *distinguido patrono.*'

They began lunch with a delicious *palta*, a salad of alligator pear stuffed with shrimps and sprinkled with lemon juice, then progressed to *empanada de horo*, a turnover filled with several kinds of meat, raisins, stuffed olives, onions, peppers and grapes. They chatted lightly about this and that, both knowing they were skirting the important issues which sooner or later would have to be aired. He waited with an indulgent smile while she scooped up the last of her strawberry ice-cream, then when coffee had been poured he spoiled her enjoyment by announcing abruptly,

'I have been in touch with my grandson by radio transmitter and have instructed him to bring his plane, which he will pilot himself, to pick us up at Santiago airport. I judge,' he glanced at his watch, 'that he will arrive in about one hour from now.'

She almost choked over her coffee. 'So soon?' she gasped.

He nodded. 'There is something I should like to

ask of you, *señorita*, before my grandson's arrival. After deep consideration I have come to the conclusion that it will be better if he is allowed to believe the child is yours – only for the time being,' he hastened to add when her head tilted with surprise. 'I will decide later when to tell him the truth.'

Carefully she set down her cup. 'But why is such deception necessary, *señor*?' she asked quietly.

Patiently she waited while he considered, his lips curving with satisfaction as he took in every facet of the picture of unspoiled innocence she was unconsciously projecting. 'Knowing my grandson as I do, and knowing his penchant for intrigue, I have decided to set him a poser. Nothing annoys him so much as an unsolved riddle, a mystery that remains unrevealed, and what could be more mysterious to a man than to be confronted with a young girl whose virtuous look is offset by the contradictory evidence of a child so like her in looks that they must obviously be related? He will naturally jump to the conclusion, as I did, that the baby is yours, and that fact,' he chuckled, 'ought to confound him as much as it confounded me.'

Serena's colour rose, but she managed to keep a rein on her temper. 'You mean, *señor*, that you wish me to pretend to be Wendy's mother in order to titillate your grandson's interest? Don't you think you're being a little unkind – both to him and to me?'

Autocratic features became, if anything, more

pronounced. 'I made no mention of kindness when our bargain was struck,' he lashed out coldly. 'Your rewards were to be strictly materialistic!'

She blanched from the icy retort, recognizing the cruelty she had once suspected lay hidden behind his façade of charm. But what he had said was true. With naïve pleasure she had accepted the benefits he had heaped upon her: expensive flight from England, the sumptuous hotel room, the very clothes she was wearing, had all been purchased by him. She had no grounds on which to complain now that the silken ropes of bondage were beginning to bite.

Her head drooped lower as she nodded brief assent. 'It shall be as you wish, *señor*, but what am I to say to your grandson without resorting to outright lies?'

'That the child is a dependant. For the time being that should be sufficient.'

She swallowed her humiliation in order to put to him a question that had been puzzling her. 'I have often wondered why you inserted that "dependants welcome" clause in your advertisement. Few people are willing to accept their employees' dependants into their homes, so why . . .?'

Reverting back to good humour now that he had got his way, he sliced off the end of a cigar and replied. 'Each word of the advertisement was carefully weighed, and the clause you mention was, I think, a touch of genius. The sort of girl for whom I was searching had to be possessed of certain qualities, the most important of which I rated a sense of duty strong enough to prevent her from betraying my trust. As a person of lesser qualities would soon have abandoned anyone likely to become a hindrance or a burden, you can follow my line of argument. I had not envisaged the dependant turning out to be a young child, but as it happens the situation falls very neatly into my plans. We never know the love our parents have for us until we become parents ourselves, which is why I mean to present my grandson with a ready-made family. One night of vigilance over a sick child will teach him more than any words of mine.'

'I'm not sure I understand,' her brow wrinkled. 'As your grandson has no memory of his parents, you must, in his eyes, have filled that role. Are you implying that he's ungrateful for the care you have lavished upon him?'

Bleakly he replied, 'Ingratitude is not the most fitting word. Let us say he has become uncertain of my motives and only by being confronted himself with the problems I have had to face during his upbringing will he begin to understand that, whatever he may have thought to the contrary, all of my actions have been carried out with only his best interests at heart.'

So long as those interests coincide with your own! Serena realized with a shock. Her skin crawled. From first meeting she had sensed the autocrat behind the kind, courteous aristocrat. He was accustomed to having his own way, to imposing his will upon weaker, less exalted mortals, but with such lack of tact, it seemed, that he had managed to alienate even his shy, obedient grandson!

Her heart sank. He was weak and so was she. What hope could the future hold for two puppets forced to dance to whatever tune their autocratic piper should decide to call?

CHAPTER FOUR

DON ALBERTO spoke little as the taxi drove them to Santiago airport. He seemed tense, a little on edge, and as they entered the airport buildings his edginess was communicated to Serena and her nervous trepidation increased a thousandfold.

In a few short minutes she was to meet the stranger she had promised to marry!

With Wendy clasped in her arms she hurried in the wake of Don Alberto, whose eyes were fastened upon a trim silver aircraft taxiing along the runway.

'Good, he has lost no time in getting here,' he muttered, his stern lips relaxing into a smile. All around them was bustling activity. Huge jets were swallowing and disgorging passengers, landing, and taking off with the consistency of buses on a busy route. But Serena had eyes for nothing other than the small silver plane and the man who had descended from it and was now striding towards them. Don Alberto's hand lifted in greeting, then dropped to his side when the man was near enough to be recognized.

'*Sacramento!*' The exclamation was laden with aggravation. 'Why have *you* come, Sosme, where is my grandson?'

44

Serena's grasp on Wendy relaxed. Obviously this was not the man for whom they had been waiting. The pilot's nervousness was betrayed by shifting eyes that travelled first to her and the baby, then back to his employer. 'He sends many pardons, *señor*, and regrets that pressure of business has prevented him from coming himself to meet you.'

'*Por Dios!*' Don Alberto was very angry. 'Then I shall expect to see a landslide or an earthquake at the very least when we arrive at the *hacienda*!'

A man-made eruption was more likely, Serena thought as she boarded the plane and took a seat next to the furious Don Alberto. For half an hour as the plane winged its way south from the capital he remained morose and silent, his regal features etched with displeasure, but when the city skyline had been left far behind and the plane was flying low over rural landscape he unbent far enough to point out long rows of eucalyptus and poplar trees stretching across the landscape; mud walls lining the roads for miles without a break and a system of canals linking dozens of connecting fields, not large in themselves, but joined by gates showing that they were all sections of the same property.

'This is some of our best farming land,' he explained. 'Because of the ideal natural conditions irrigation development is not expensive, many of the Chilean rivers rise in the snow fields of the high Andes and as a result the water supply is ample, even during the dry summer.'

45

Nervously she cleared her throat. 'Do you raise crops, *señor?*'

'Not on a commercial scale,' he replied. 'Our land is more suitable for the rearing of livestock. We have gardens and orchards around the *hacienda*, of course; but they yield only enough for our own needs.'

Once again he lapsed into silence and Serena grew more and more tense as cultivated land gave way to miles and miles of grassland upon which thousands of head of grazing cattle spread an undulating, never-ending carpet of brown bodies across the landscape. Never in her life had she seen so many animals herded together and when the mass finally petered out and the plane began dipping towards a house just visible on the horizon she had no need of Don Alberto's terse instructions to tell her that they had finally arrived.

On legs that threatened to fold up under her, she alighted from the aircraft and settled into the back of the car which then began driving them towards a great rambling house set in a grove of giant eucalyptus trees. Against a background of distant mountains the house nestled into a terraced hillside, its walls made up of stone quarried out of the same hillside on which it stood. The cement pointing of the stonework was recessed, not flush with the walls, giving a simple effect of dry stone walls exactly like those surrounding an almond orchard in the background. The stark white of the building made an

46

excellent foil for a green pantiled roof, and square green tiles surrounding a swimming pool and the floor of a covered terrace.

When they moved indoors Serena saw that the same square tiles had been used for the floors, continuing the absolute simplicity of the outside architecture. Don Alberto guided her out of the cool hall into a salon carpeted in a soft shade of tan that picked up the main colour of the linen-upholstered banquettes lining three of the walls. Behind them ran white shelves holding a scattering of books, exquisite ornaments and, here and there, slim elegant lamps blended into the simple, uncluttered background. The focal point of the room was an open fireplace set square in the centre of a raised marble flag large enough to seat a dozen people with, descending directly from above, a huge copper canopy which would glisten fiery orange, yellow and red when bathed by leaping flames.

Pleased by her wide-eyed wonder, Don Alberto questioned,

'You like my home, *señorita?*'

Serena's glistening eyes were response enough. 'It's beautiful, *señor*. You're to be congratulated on the way you've introduced modern amenities into an old house without ruining its character.'

He acknowledged the compliment with a nod, but before he could reply a woman burst into the salon, a small, stout woman waving her arms in agitated greeting.

'*Pardone*, Señor Conde, that stupid Cosme has just this moment informed me of your arrival. You will require refreshments, drinks for the lady and yourself and milk for *la niña*?'

'*Gracias*, Carmen, I'm certain our guests must be parched as I am myself. But before you serve drinks perhaps it would be as well if you show the Señorita Payne up to her room. You have prepared a nursery as I instructed?'

'*Si, señor*,' Carmen nodded vigorously, her dark eyes set curiously upon Serena and the child in her arms. 'It is all ready and waiting, if the *señorita* will follow me?'

Don Alberto delayed their exit. 'And the nurse-maid, you have found someone suitable?'

'That, too, has been taken care of, *señor*. The daughter of Cosme, who has many small brothers and sisters, was eager to undertake the nursing of the *pequeña*.'

'Excellent, then all is satisfactory.' He smiled at Serena. 'Forgive me if I do not join you for refreshments, I have business affairs to catch up on, but we will dine together this evening when I hope to be able to introduce my absentee grandson who will, I feel sure, apologize profusely for omitting to be present upon your arrival.'

'Please don't worry about me, *señor*,' she returned, made uneasy by the tightness of his smile. 'Carry on with your work, I shall be quite happy exploring my new surroundings. And as for your grandson's absence, it has already been explained. I shall look forward to joining both of you for dinner.'

Suppressing the panic such a thought aroused, Serena set off in Carmen's wake hugging a drowsy Wendy tightly to her breast, reminding herself that now her objective had been reached – beautiful, luxurious surroundings in which a child could grow up happy and contented – she must not shirk the task of having to pay, however high the price.

Carmen chatted non-stop as she showed her around the rooms that were to be hers and Wendy's. Both the bedroom and nursery were tucked under the eaves, with roof beams sloping down to white-washed walls whose nooks and crannies had been in-geniously adapted into built-in wardrobes and bookshelves. A long, wide shelf running directly beneath a window lent itself admirably for use as a writing desk.

The nursery connecting with her bedroom was equally cool and airy, with decorative wrought iron grilles fitted across windows thrown wide open to frame a patch of heavenly blue sky and to admit pure, blossom-scented air. As she handed the sleepy child into the arms of a young girl Carmen had introduced as Bella, Serena's sense of elation grew. If she had sought the world over she could not have found a more perfect place in which to live and nothing and no one, she decided, was going to sep-arate them from this child's paradise of orchards in which to play, animals with which to frolic, and glorious clean air in which to thrive.

The rest of the afternoon and early evening she spent investigating the immediate surroundings of the *hacienda*. She wandered down to an empty corral and stood leaning against the top bar of a fence, wondering how many horses were accommodated within its large enclosure. At this very moment men and riders were no doubt riding the pampas, sorting, branding, keeping watch over the immense herds she had seen from the plane. Leisurely she strolled around, peeping once into a huge bunkhouse and finding it deserted. But from a nearby cookhouse she heard the rattle of pots and pans, then later a delicious aroma of roast beef assailed her nostrils. Preparations were under way for a huge meal, so obviously the riders were expected to return within the hour.

The sun was inclining towards the horizon when she hurried back to the *hacienda*. Feeling benevolently disposed towards the man whose need of her was the essence of her good fortune, she selected from her wardrobe a dress she thought might appeal to a shy, inhibited young man. It was of midnight blue velvet, high-necked, long-sleeved, with a skirt that clung to her hips and whispered seductively around slim feet encased in silver strapped sandals. Heavy golden waves were brushed so vigorously that her scalp tingled, but the shimmering curtain of hair curling on to her shoulders amply rewarded the extra effort, she considered, preening for a second in front of a mirror before venturing downstairs.

She had just nerved herself to take the first tentative steps when the quiet of the evening was shattered by the thunder of hooves descending upon the *hacienda*, together with a whooping, yelling horde of riders who dismounted and made their boisterous way in the direction of the cookhouse. As Serena hesitated, hard footsteps resounded on the floor of the veranda beneath her window; one of the dismounted riders striding into the house, his steps accompanied by the jingling of spurs. Seconds later there came a murmuring of voices that escalated into a storm of angry words, unintelligible, but disturbing as the rumbling of thunder. She could just distinguish the cold, autocratic tone of Don Alberto and a second, equally decisive voice slicing through his argument with the thrust of a rapier. Startled, she moved towards the window in a bid to identify Don Alberto's unknown antagonist. What man was daring to raise his voice to the elderly *hidalgo* who ruled his world with a fist of steel? Surely no ordinary man! No employee would chance such utter recklessness.

The hail of angry words was severed by the sound of a door slamming so viciously the foundations of the *hacienda* shuddered. Silence fell, a silence into which Serena drew a long frightened breath as reaction against the aura of barely restrained violence.

She was nerving herself once more to going downstairs when her bedroom door crashed wide open and a tall, black-clad figure strode into her bedroom. Speechless, she stared, her startled eyes questioning his invasion of privacy.

Arrogantly her stare was returned. He stood with feet apart, balancing on heels encased in decorative silver spurs, his long, leather-clad legs seeming to stretch forever before reaching hips slim, hard and muscled. A black shirt slashed at the neck revealed a chest tanned toast brown and a strong column of throat supported a head of wind-tossed hair, black as Satan's heart, matching eyes diabolically gleaming over a blade of nose with nostrils stretched taut with anger. Cruel lips quirked upwards in mock amusement revealing a snap of white teeth as he bit out,

'So, you are the latest addition to the stud!' His eyes denigrated her shrinking figure. 'I might have guessed El Conde's mind would run upon the lines of a milk-and-water miss, spirited as a mouse and sexless as a plaster madonna!'

Serena gasped at the onslaught. 'Who are you?' she quavered. 'How dare you burst into my room without so much as a—'

'Don't insult my intelligence!' he interrupted brusquely. 'Outraged virtue is hardly an attitude conversant with a woman who, according to my grandfather, is more than willing to share my bed!'

A scalding race of colour accompanied sickening recognition. 'You mean *you* are—'

'No other than your reluctant *esposo*.' He swept a

mocking bow. 'Don Juan de Valdivia, the second pawn in my grandfather's unthinkable game.'

'Pawn . . . game . . .?' she stammered.

He strode forward until she was engulfed by his shadow, narowly searching the small, distrait face for a hint of duplicity. Without softening, he declared, 'It is just possible that you are not aware of my grandfather's scheme – indeed, I am not surprised that he is ashamed to speak of it. Sit down, *señorita*, there is something you ought to know.'

Serena almost collapsed into a chair, clasping her arms around her shuddering body in an effort to dispel her slowly creeping fear of this overpowering individual, every bit as daunting as the grandfather he so obviously despised. Gone were her illusions of a shy introvert, and in his place a man so divorced from her imaginings she felt she would prefer to face fire, plague and pestilence rather than become tied for life to this cold-eyed, uncivilized cowboy possessed of all the savagery of his *conquistador* ancestors.

'My grandfather,' he spat, 'is renowned throughout the land for his exceptional successes in the breeding of livestock. Because he has devoted most of his life to the study of strain and temperament he can now proudly boast of his ability to produce a specific strain to order, whether the demand be for the quietly docile or the viciously brave he undertakes to deliver with satisfaction guaranteed or money refunded. Such is his conceit, he has now decided to apply his skill to humans. Oh, yes,' he affirmed when she gasped a protest. 'Because he succeeded once in such an exercise he has decided to try again!

'Like me,' he went on, 'my father was reputedly headstrong and wilful, preferring to make his own mistakes rather than benefit from the advice of his omnipotent father. Then out of the blue a girl descended upon the hacienda, an English girl, blueeyed, blonde, docile, chosen especially to appeal to the better side of my father's flamboyant nature. I am told they fell in love, although I suspect that initially my mother was more in love with her luxurious surroundings than she was with my father. It must have been a great annoyance to my grandfather when an earthquake prevented him from thoroughly researching his experiment. Doubtless that is why he is anxious to try again and this time, *señorita*, you and I are the subjects upon whom his plans concentrate.'

His chin jutted as softly he taunted, 'How does it feel to know you have been chosen solely to act as a mellowing influence, to tone down my abrasive qualities so that I may become more receptive to my grandfather's commands? I warn you now,' he continued, 'it will not work! You will find it easier to tame the condor — our flying eagle of the Andes — than you will to press your slender little foot upon my neck!'

Serena backed away from his vehemence, holding

a hand to her madly thumping heart. 'I have no wish to put my foot upon your neck, *señor*,' she denied shakily. 'I came here because I thought you needed me. I imagined,' her words broke on an incredulous croak, 'that you were a shy, introverted young man who was unable to nerve himself to find a wife. I see now that your grandfather painted a totally misleading picture of the man he wished me to marry. I couldn't marry *you*, *señor*, I'd rather starve!'

Her brave ultimatum seared his pride. Furiously he stared down at her, taking his time, his contempt no less obvious because it was mute. She withdrew from the lean body with its suggestion of curbed violence and walked across to the window out of range of his voiceless contempt.

'Would you please go now, *señor*?' she requested across a stiffly-held shoulder.

Hauteur from the meek little mouse was the last thing he had expected. He strode across and grabbed her shoulder, spinning her round with a grip so vicious she only just withheld a pained cry. 'Why did you allow yourself to be talked into coming here?' he demanded. 'You have beauty enough to appeal to some men, so lack of suitors could not have been the deciding factor. Did he offer you money? Ah, I see that he did!' He released his hold with a swiftness that underlined his revulsion and strode away, halting when he reached the door to throw out a last bitter observation,

'As my grandfather bought you, you are his responsibility and he must decide what is to be done with you. Heed my advice, *señorita*, leave as soon as possible. We have no need of you here!'

He was stepping across the threshold when a cry came from the direction of the nursery. Immediately he was forgotten as Serena hastened towards the connecting door, mindful of the fact that she had told Bella to go for her meal and that Wendy was alone. As she tiptoed across to the cot Wendy's cry changed to a mischievous gurgle and when Serena picked her up she began blowing childish bubbles of pleasure.

'You little fraud!' Serena scolded fondly. 'If I'm not careful, young lady, you'll be in danger of becoming spoiled.'

'To whom does the child belong?' The bleak question reached across the dusk-shadowed room, reminding her that they had an audience.

She spun round, a picture of youthful innocence, her madonna-like beauty highlighted by the child she held in her arms.

'To me,' she replied calmly, mindful of the promise Don Alberto had extracted.

'You?' He rocked on his heels.

'Yes,' she confirmed, taking wicked delight in his astonishment.

'And the father, where is he?'

The catch in her voice was genuine when she replied, 'Her father is dead.'

His swift glance at her ringless fingers betrayed the direction of his thoughts, but she did not care, all she wanted was to be rid of the man with the abrasive manner that made her feel shame even though there was no cause.

But he moved closer, close enough to come within the orbit of Wendy's limpid blue eyes. She had no inhibitions about showing her approval of the strange man, even though his appraising eyes held no encouragement. Brazenly, she blew a wet kiss in his direction and held out her arms as an invitation to him to give her a cuddle. Serena almost laughed aloud at his expression of bafflement, wishing it was herself and not her sister who was the cause of his disconcertion. But the tone of her voice held a warning to behave as she placed Wendy back in her cot and reproved tartly, 'Time you were asleep, young madam. No, you're not to sit up!' She pressed Wendy back against her pillow and bent to give her a kiss. 'Good night, darling, I'll see you in the morning.'

She walked out of the nursery, indicating that Juan Valdivia should follow, and waited until he was inside her room before firmly closing the connecting door.

'Have you any other family besides the child?'

His abrupt question took her by surprise. 'None,' she answered truthfully. 'But don't let that fact worry you, *señor*, wherever Wendy and I are together is home.'

Savagely he glared into her composed face, his jaw muscles working as he fought to contain some aggravation that was bedevilling him. 'The old one is as devious as the devil,' he muttered, 'but not even these circumstances will force me to change my mind!'

He was gone before she could ask him to explain, swallowing up the length of the passageway with giant strides, his spurs jangling deep exasperation in his wake.

CHAPTER FIVE

WHEN the sound of the dinner-gong reverberated through the house Serena felt like running away, but its summons had to be obeyed because even though she had no intention of remaining at the *hacienda*, a confrontation with Don Alberto was inevitable. He owed her explanations and, if he were gentleman enough, an apology for his misleading description of his grandson's character.

She prayed for strength as she hurried down the stairs, nerving herself for a second helping of scorn from eyes so stormy she felt battered by their hail. Shuddering nerves delayed her as she hesitated outside the door, then with great courage she pushed it open and stepped inside the salon.

It was an anti-climax to find that only Don Alberto was present, staring moodily into a glass of golden Madeira. He rose to his feet when she entered, his features betraying no sign of shame as he moved forward to greet her.

'You are looking very lovely, *señorita*, and I thank you, it is many years since such beauty has graced my table.'

She steeled herself against softening. 'You are very gracious, *señor*, but you must forgive me if I find your compliments as suspect as some of your previous statements.'

His tall figure drew erect, but she refused to be dominated by the hauteur of a man who had not hesitated to deceive her. She sensed a sharp reply hovering on his lips, but then his mouth softened and as he drew her forward he confessed wryly,

'I do owe you an apology, señorita. To withhold the truth is perhaps a greater sin than to tell a deliberate lie. But before we talk, let me pour you a glass of wine. Dinner can wait until you are in a more amicable mood to appreciate it.'

She waved away his offer of wine but allowed him to guide her towards a settee into which she sank, her apprehensive eyes drawn as if magnetized towards the door.

'Relax, cara,' he murmured. 'My grandson has left the hacienda with his huaso friends to pay a visit to a nearby town. I have no doubt that it will be early morning before the sound of their usually boisterous arrival is heard.'

Fluid with relief, Serena relaxed against the cushions, a reaction he seemed to find amusing.

'So, already you have met my grandson?'

'Met is an understatement,' she answered shakily, 'It would be more accurate to say that I was cornered, lassoed and immediately branded.'

In the process of pouring out her unwanted drink he hesitated, one regal eyebrow raised. 'Branded?' he frowned.

'Branded a bought woman, señor,' she explained. 'One who, according to your grandson, has no place here and whose destiny must be decided by her purchaser, namely yourself.'

'*Por Dios!*' The exclamation ripped from lips thin with anger. 'Were he still a boy he would be severely punished for such an insult!'

'But he is not a boy, and, in any case, I feel he was justified in speaking as he did. To choose a wife for a grandson who is shy and uncertain is perhaps not so unreasonable, but to choose a wife for a man such as Don Juan is nothing short of foolish. Surely, *señor*, you know your grandson well enough to realize such an action was bound to arouse his intense resentment?'

His reply, as he took a seat next to her, was no more than a sigh. A sigh of regret that he had not got his way, she wondered, or a sigh of remorse for the injury he had inflicted upon both his grandson and herself?

'If you will allow me to explain,' he begged, 'my motives might appear less selfish.'

'Your motives have already been explained by your grandson. He has told me of your successes with the breeding of livestock and of the obsessive conceit that has led you to assume you can define which two human creatures are most likely to blend into a successful partnership. In this instance, *señor*, you could not have been more wrong. Don Juan is one of a type I detest – boorish, uncivilized and totally self-centred!'

To her surprise, Don Alberto's eyes lit up and a smile broke the symmetry of his stern mouth. Annoyed by his amusement, Serena jumped to her feet, but he detained her with a placating hand.

'Forgive me, *cara*, but I have heard those words before, expressed equally vehemently and equally sincerely. They were spoken by the girl who was later to become my son's wife, one who I admit was detained deliberately at the *hacienda* for the same purpose as yourself. As a young man my son was just as untameable as is Juan. His every working day was spent on the pampas in the company of *huasos* whose freedom he envied. Not for him the responsibility of running what amounts to a small republic within a republic, not for him the worries, the decision making, the stresses and strains connected with the running of a large business! Many girls of good family were willing, indeed eager, to become his wife, but he would have none of them, preferring the unrestricting company of women – I hesitate to call them ladies – who frequent the *posadas* – taverns – of the nearby town that is similarly exploited by my grandson and his friends.

'Unlike you,' he told her, 'the girl was not carefully chosen but arrived here quite by accident, although I must confess that at first sight of her the germ of an idea was born, an idea which I nurtured and implemented by throwing them together as much as possible. Initially they were antagonistic towards each other, but later, to my delight, the attachment I had foreseen developed and grew into a love that completely revolutionized my son's character. They were intensely happy, *señorita*, and my grief when that happiness was terminated cannot be expressed in words. Juan is a legacy of that happiness, and my dearest wish is to see him make an equally happy marriage before I die. You may think I am trying to play God,' he concluded simply, 'but can you blame me for duplicating the circumstances that led up to such a marriage – a marriage of which Juan is living proof of its worth?'

Serena stood up and moved slowly across to the fireplace. Firelight flickered upon her downbent head and cast shadows across her perturbed face as she considered with emotions of amazement and pity the confessions of a ruler of a small kingdom whose life style and wealth had convinced him he possessed the omnipotence of a king. *El rey de los guasos!* King of the cowboys! She stifled an hysterical laugh at the thought that when he abdicated he wished her to become queen!

But there was no trace of amusement on the face she turned towards the elderly *hidalgo* sitting with bowed head resting upon an upturned palm. Gently, because she had no wish to hurt, she told him,

'I'm sorry, *señor*, but I can play no part in your fantasy – and a fantasy it is,' she assured him quickly when his head snapped up in protest. 'Everyone has a right to live his life as he sees fit, your grandson included. I am convinced that your motives are unselfish and that your dearest wish is for your grandson's happiness, but have you ever considered,' deep blue eyes earnestly pleaded, 'that the success of your first scheme might have been a fluke and that no amount of duplication would produce the same result?'

Her doubt cast a reflection upon his reputation and ignited a spark of anger. 'Human nature does not change, *señorita*! Century after century, the human race has duplicated itself over and over again, the same traits, the same vices, the same characteristics have all been passed down from family to family. In my veins runs the blood of early *conquistadors*, my inheritance of adventurous nature, fearlessness and pride was handed down to me from my father, then passed to my son and in return to my grandson. My understanding of them both stems from the fact that each inherited a part of me, they reacted as I would react, liked what I liked, shared my dislikes. So you see there is no way in which I could be mistaken.'

'But there is,' she contradicted quietly, clasping trembling fingers hard. 'There is the unknown element to which you have given no thought, the outsider who is an essential part of your plan, namely myself! Without my co-operation you can achieve nothing and I have no intention of becoming a part of such a conspiracy. I wish to be released from my promise. I would like to return home immediately, preferably without ever having to meet your grandson again!'

Without haste Don Alberto disposed of his empty glass and strode regally towards her. Feeling like a lowly serf in the presence of an intimidating monarch, Serena was tempted to drop him a curtsey as he towered above her, registering deep displeasure.

'That will not be possible,' he informed her, cold and unapproachable as the ice-capped peaks overlooking his kingdom. 'A bargain was struck and already you have accepted part of the price offered. The clothes you wear, the home in which you and your sister are now established, are part of that price and I must insist upon a fair return. As you will already have discovered, the *hacienda* is completely cut off from the world, so any foolhardy thought of escape can be banished from your mind. The only safe method of transport is by plane, and as our private aircraft will definitely not be put at your disposal you will remain here whether you like it or not!'

White with shock, she gasped, 'You can force me to stay, but you will never force me to marry your grandson!'

Imperturbably he countered, 'In the beginning, your predecessor was every bit as unco-operative, so it pleases me that you should be the same. Your identical reaction augurs well for the success of my plan.'

Moonlight streamed through the window on to the bed where Serena had thrown herself hours earlier after fleeing from the autocrat whose determination had filled her with dread. The house she had loved at first sight now seemed a prison and her bedroom a cell in which to reflect upon her crime. The crime of folly, she berated herself, her clenched fists digging deep wells into the silken covers. *'Fool, fool!'* she sobbed, 'to think the favours you sought could be paid for without pain!' Not that she had not been prepared to pay – she had, but with willingness and understanding towards a very different man from the one who held her in such contempt he had ordered her departure.

Smothering an anguished sob, she dragged herself from the bed and began fumbling with the fasteners of the blue dress, anxious to be rid of the costly bribe. For the first time in her life she was feeling self-contempt and not even the reminder that her actions had been carried out on Wendy's behalf could heal the sore of disgust festering inside.

Clad only in a thin slip, she sat gazing out of the window with unseeing eyes, her mind drowned to numbness by her storm of bitter tears. A slight jingling sound assailed her ears, but she dismissed it as an echo of past torment. Then the sound came again and this time she spun round, her frightened eyes probing the dusk-filled room. Terror kept her rooted to the spot when a patch of shadow moved, then moonlight sliced a path through the dimness and glistened upon a large silver buckle clasped against a lean, belted waist. She had seen the buckle before, its intricate design had attracted her attention even while turbulent words were being exchanged with its owner!

She found her voice. 'What do you want? How dare you come uninvited into my bedroom, Don Juan!'

Her heart sank when he laughed, low, reckless laughter that spelled out his contempt of convention. His lean length swayed as he swaggered towards her.

'I have come to tell you that after giving a great deal of thought to our predicament,' he mocked, 'I have found a solution.'

Sickened, she realized that he had been drinking, and cheap perfume wafting from his shirt proved that he had not spent the night alone.

'I, too, have come to a decision,' she tilted. 'I have decided that I have no wish to stay here and the only thing I wish to hear from you is a promise that you will help me to return home.'

He unnverved her by reaching out to pinion her shoulders with rough, unkind hands. She shivered when his fingers began exploring the smooth curve of uncovered flesh, but stood stock-still under his hands, determined not to give him the satisfaction of seeing her cringe.

'But that would not fall in at all well with my plans!' he refused. 'I have decided that I will marry you – not as an act of surrender, but to teach my grandfather a lesson, to prove to him that a marriage conceived by the devil must result in a life of hell, hell for him, hell for his accomplice, but for me the satisfaction of knowing that since I have complied with his wishes he will be honour bound to fulfil his promise!'

'Promise? What promise . . .?' The question tore from her painfully constricted throat.

'His promise to hand over to me my inheritance, what else?' His voice held a hateful slur. 'Ever since boyhood I have been brought up to believe that one day all this would be mine. Because of that belief I have ridden hard, driven hard, and worked until callouses stood out on my hands, satisfied that the ownership of the *hacienda* was to be my reward! Then my grandfather dropped his bombshell – marriage or else . . .! Not marriage to a woman of my choice but to one of his, and the outcome of my refusal was to be banishment from the place I had been taught to consider my own. But together, *señorita*, we will fool the old fox! Let him preen himself in the knowledge that he has had his way, let him gloat in his mastery for the short time he has left. He is old, that one!' His tone adopted a sombre intensity that made her shudder. 'In a few years' time, perhaps less, he will die, then you and I will go our separate ways. But for the time being I am willing to go through a form of ceremony, to promise to love, cherish and keep you. Not that I intend keeping to those promises,' he jeered. 'My life will not alter in any way, but I am sure that will not worry you, *señorita*. Marriage and an honourable name will, I'm sure, be compensation enough for a secondhand bride!'

Serena reacted to the insult as if she had been struck. Almost she poured out her disgust, her scorn of him, and the truth that would have restored her pride. Then instinct warned her that this facet of the proposed marriage was the one he found most distasteful. Don Juan Valdivia would insist always upon being the first and only man in the life of his bride, and Wendy's presence would be proof to all that he was but second choice, a position his haughty nature would find intolerable.

Torn between the dominance of two men, both striving towards the same objective, she knew it would be useless to rebel, but by remaining silent she would not be alone in her torment. He, too, would suffer! For the first time in her life Serena savoured the taste of revenge — and found the flavour sweet!

'Well, what do you have to say?' he demanded. 'Are you willing to help me confound the old fox?'

'Do I have a choice?' she questioned with cold disdain.

His probing eyes scoured her pale face. Beneath his hands Serena remained rigid, schooling her features into a mask of calm. He uttered a sharp derisive laugh. 'Your distant beauty chills to the bone, *señorita*! Compared with the women of my own race you are but a shadow of femininity, you lack their voluptuous fire, their willingness to please and the ripe wantonness of their bodies. You need not worry that marriage to me will mean sharing my bed – I can think of nothing less pleasing than the prospect of having kisses turn to ice upon my lips and the risk of frostbite accompanying every caress!' He thrust her from him with such indifference that Serena was stung to anger.

'I understand your revulsion, *señor*, because it exactly matches my own! Nothing revolts me more than the thought of being in close proximity to a man who has over-indulged in wine to such an extent that his speech has become slurred and his actions unsteady. The vine bears three kinds of grapes, the first of pleasure, the next of intoxication, and the third of disgust!'

Her scorn cracked like a whip across his pride. He jerked erect, then pounced, lifting her like a piece of thistledown against his chest. 'You will apologize for those insults,' he gritted, 'or risk being punished!'

'Put me down!' she hissed, feeling desperately for the floor beneath her flailing feet.

'Not until you do as I say,' was his grim reply.

'Why should I apologize for speaking the truth? I ask no apology from you, yet your words were both ungentlemanly and insulting.'

'Ungentlemanly!' He threw back his head and

laughed. 'That is one thing I have never claimed to be! After all, what is a gentleman but a man made up wholly of the dove without the least sting of the serpent in his composition? Is that the type of man you admire, *señorita*, a cooing, spiritless dove?'

'If the choice be so narrow, then yes, I do prefer a man who would try force only when persuasion had failed.'

'Whereas I consider force does away with the need for persuasion!' To demonstrate his point he swooped upon her parted lips to inflict a kiss that was no more than a fiery brand, cruel, hurtful and totally lacking in emotion. Remembering his predilection for women of fire and passion, Serena forced herself not to struggle while he carried out his punishment. To have struggled would have pleased him, whereas her ice-cold acceptance poured scorn upon his brutal actions.

Without regret, he lifted his mouth from hers and relaxed his hold. Swaggering towards the door, he tossed across his shoulder,

'Keep your kisses, ice maiden! I am at a loss to know whether to admire or despise the man who had nerve enough to tear the veil from the eyes of the novice and lead her into motherhood!'

CHAPTER SIX

THE wedding took place a week later in a private chapel situated within the boundaries of the *hacienda*. The guest list was kept to a minimum – not, Don Alberto assured Serena, from choice, but because the hastily-arranged ceremony had made it impossible for branches of the family resident in Spain to be contacted in time to attend. So only close friends residing within the vicinity had been invited to be present at the marriage of Don Alberto's grandson and an unknown English girl whose arrival, accompanied by a child, had given rise to much speculation.

All invitations had been accepted, mainly at the instigation of curious mamas intent upon seeing for themselves the girl who had snatched the much-sought-after bachelor from under the noses of their resentful daughters.

During the week preceding the wedding Don Alberto had carried out all the arrangements wearing a smile reminiscent of that upon the face of a tiger. His surprise at Juan's sudden capitulation had been as great as was his reaction to Serena's adamant demand that his grandson should be kept permanently in the dark about her relationship with Wendy.

'But why, *niña?*' he had cried. 'The very presence of the child must be a thorn in his side! Why not be kind and rid him of the doubts that must be plaguing him?'

'I have no wish to be kind to your grandson,' she had retorted. 'You are holding me forcibly to our bargain and I have had no option but to agree to the marriage, but on this one condition I stand firm — either my secret is kept or the marriage will not take place.'

To Don Alberto it was an insignificant point on which to argue. His goal was in sight, the players had been positioned, the set was staged exactly to his liking, so he was not prepared to tolerate any last-minute hitches.

'Very well,' he had submitted brusquely, 'if that is your wish then so be it.' Thoughtfully, he had fingered his chin, then a slow smile had transformed his downcast mouth. 'Your way might possibly turn out to be the best. We are neither of us fools, *niña*, both of us are aware that Juan has agreed to the marriage not because he is in love with you, but for some hidden reason of his own. It may be that you attract him without his being conscious of it, even pity could be behind his decision, but whatever the reason I am prepared to rely upon feminine intuition to find the quickest way to his heart. Yes, *cara*, keep your secret, by all means! We Valdivia men are savagely possessive of our women, and if the thorn is left to fester it will be a constant reminder

73

that his wife once belonged to another man.'

A second-hand bride, Serena reflected numbly as she fumbled with the dozen small buttons fastening the bodice of the cream lace dress she had chosen to wear for the ceremony. It was short, full-skirted and lined with heavy cream silk except for the sleeves which had been left transparent so that delicate lace scrolls were etched upon creamy skin from shoulder to wrist. She had brushed her hair back severely from her brow, then twisted it into a rope of burnished gold that encircled her small head like a noose – like the silken noose, she reflected wryly, with which her independence was being slowly strangled.

A scattering of small white blossoms lessened the severity of her hair-style, but beneath the burnished crown her face looked pinched and white, her eyes shadowed by the enormity of the step she was about to take. She had remained in her room all morning and drifting through her open window she had heard the sounds of much activity as guests had arrived and been greeted before being ushered inside for refreshments. Most of them, Don Alberto had told her, had travelled by private plane or, in the case of near neighbours, in limousines powerful enough to eat up the miles of road linking the properties.

Beneath Serena's feet the *hacienda* had seemed to hum with activity, but in her frozen state she had not dared venture downstairs lest curious looks should disturb the composure she had striven so hard to cement. Besides that, there was one small tradition she wished to follow, a laughable tradition in the circumstances, but one which nevertheless she meant to carry out. She had urgent need of luck if she were to survive the trauma of marriage to Don Juan and if, as it was said, it was unlucky for the bridegroom to catch sight of his bride immediately before the ceremony then she was determined to keep out of his way.

At the sounds of guests departing for the church her nerves tightened and the butterflies in her stomach went berserk. She had eaten little, not even Carmen's anxious scolding had induced her to tackle any more than a piece of toast and a mouthful of coffee. Now, as the last of the guests drove away from the *hacienda*, she suffered a wave of weakness and clutched hard on the back of a chair, willing herself not to faint. A tap on her door set her heart racing and a few seconds elapsed before she was able to call a quavering, 'Come in!'

Carmen entered, flushed and excited, bearing in her hands a swathe of fine cream lace. With old-world subservience she dropped Serena a curtsey, then offered,

'The mantilla, *señorita*, that has been worn by all Valdivia brides.'

Serena backed away as if stung. 'No, thank you, Carmen, I shall go as I am.'

Carmen's black button eyes enlarged with shock.

'But it is forbidden to enter into church without first covering the head, *señorita!* And a bride's face should always be shielded from prying eyes . . . see, I will drape it over your head to show how becoming is the headdress of our race!'

Before Serena could protest she had whipped the mantilla over her head and begun arranging the scalloped edges so that most of her ashen cheeks were concealed.

'*Muy fino, señorita!*' she cried. '*Es bueno?*'

'Yes, it does look well,' Serena reluctantly conceded, sweeping downcast lashes across tormented eyes. 'But Don Alberto might object to my wearing such a delicate heirloom. It is far too fragile to be used.'

Carmen shook her head. 'El Conde will deny nothing to his grandson's *bellisima esposa!*'

Beautiful betrothed! Her breath caught in a gasp of pain. If that were true she would have no need to feel the wearing of the mantilla would be an act of desecration.

Beaming her satisfaction, Carmen urged, 'El Conde awaits you downstairs, the house is now deserted except for ourselves, the last of the guests left for the church some time ago.'

'And Don Juan, where is he?' Serena choked.

'Waiting impatiently at the altar, no doubt,' Carmen chuckled, 'but not for much longer! You have barely five minutes before you are due to leave.'

Slowly Serena descended the staircase, holding on to the banisters to give support to her trembling knees. As Carmen had said, the house was deserted, but the pungent aroma of cigars and expensive perfume still wafted in the air, reminding her of the barrage of eyes she was shortly to face.

Don Alberto was waiting patiently in the salon and upon hearing her soft footfall he spun round to welcome her warmly.

'A beautiful day for a beautiful bride, *mia cara*! You are looking exceptionally lovely, Don Juan will be the envy of all his friends!'

He drew her towards the window, then left her gazing out at the sun-drenched garden while he walked across to his desk and began rummaging in a drawer. Serena was startled when his voice spoke close to her ear.

'These are my wedding present to you, it will please me greatly if you will wear them for the ceremony.' Taking a strand of pearls from their nest of velvet, he draped them around her neck and after fumbling for a while with the diamond clasp he grunted his satisfaction, then guided her across to a mirror to let her see for herself the subdued beauty of rainbow-tinted jewels glowing against the cream bodice of her dress.

'Thank you, they're quite lovely,' she intoned woodenly, 'but now that you are about to achieve your desire there's no need to continue showering me with expensive gifts – a home for Wendy and myself is payment enough.'

He frowned, disliking the reminder of a bargain he was now prepared to forget. 'The pearls are not a payment, merely an attempt to show an old man's gratitude and his pleasure in welcoming you into his family. Which reminds me, now that we are almost related, please address me as Abuelito. I would be honoured if you could bring yourself to look upon me as a grandfather – both yourself and *La niña,* who in a mere week has endeared herself to all whom she has encountered.'

A fleeting smile touched her lips. What he had said was so true. In some magical way Wendy seemed to have sensed that she was now settled in a permanent home with adoring slaves all around her. Don Alberto himself took every opportunity that was offered to hold her and speak with her. Bella and Carmen were putty in her hands, and even Juan responded with a slow smile to her engaging advances. She made a target of him whenever he strode into her vicinity. Like a puppy bestowing allegiance to but one master, she responded to his presence by ignoring everyone else and concentrating great blue eyes in his direction, cooing and blowing kisses with shameles abandon until he was forced to respond. With the awkwardness of a man unused to children, he would send a nod in her direction. But once, in an unguarded moment, Serena had surprised him playing furtively with Wendy, throwing her a soft ball and chucking her under the chin until she had been reduced to an ecstasy of laughter.

It was Juan who had insisted that Wendy had to be present at the ceremony, so ten minutes earlier she had been driven to the church in Bella's arms, looking angelic in a dress the colour of her eyes, smocked with white, her pale golden curls rioting around a ribbon of matching blue.

'Come, my dear, it is time for us to go.' Don Alberto's touch shocked Serena into reality. 'And may I say how deeply grateful I am to be allowed, for this one day, to take the place of the father you so recently lost.'

Tears of pain and gratitude spurted to her eyes and rapidly she blinked them away. The charm of the old gentleman was such that she had to keep reminding herself of the injustice he had done her. At this moment her resentment should have been at full flood, but instead it had ebbed away, leaving her vulnerable to his persuasive tongue. But as they walked outside to the car in which Don Alberto himself was to drive them to the church, Carmen's emotional farewell was almost her undoing. In a rush of maternal concern, she enfolded Serena in her arms and with tears streaming down her cheeks kissed her fervently, murmuring unintelligible Spanish sentiments which were nevertheless recognizable as tributes to a beautiful young bride.

When Carmen's lips touched her cheek Serena almost lost control, the maternal caress reminding her poignantly of her mother. An intense longing to have her by her side on this day of all days shot through her, leaving her weak and shaken. Through this breach in her defences her tears found outlet, huge drops of misery that shimmered in her eyes, reminding Don Alberto of a storm sweeping over a placid blue lake.

A crisp white handkerchief was thrust into her hand, but when the storm showed little sign of abating he was forced to remind her, 'Our guests are waiting, *cara*. Juan also, and patience cannot be numbered amongst his virtues.'

He admired courage and was not slow to recognize it when her slight figure drew erect and her head lifted to display an outthrust chin. 'I'm sorry,' her voice was not quite steady, 'I'm ready now.'

Carmen waved from the steps of the gaily decorated, bunting-hung *hacienda* until the car was almost out of sight. She had been left behind to supervise the serving of food and drink to the guests who would be returning for the wedding lunch. As they drove, Serena noticed coloured lights strung out between the trees in readiness for the outdoor barbecue that was to take place later in the evening for the benefit of the *huasos* and their families, too numerous to be accommodated indoors.

'You will like our church, *niña*,' Don Alberto encouraged her during the five-minute drive. 'It was built by our early ancestors as an offering to God for the many benefits bestowed upon them in their new country. We have worshipped there for centuries and all Valdivia marriages have taken place there. It pleases me greatly that Juan and yourself are continuing the tradition.'

For one wild moment she was tempted to laugh in his face. He was treating this marriage as if it were a genuine love match instead of a carefully conceived plan. He was being blindly obtuse, preferring to believe what he wished to believe, hoping that eventually imagination would become fact.

Then suddenly the air was rent with cries and in the distance a rapidly approaching cloud of dust began solidifying into a horde of wildly galloping horsemen who surrounded the car whooping and yelling like screaming dervishes. The *huasos* had come to escort her. Each was wearing a colourful poncho, a broad-brimmed sombrero, tight-fitting black leather leggings buckled on above the knees and high-heeled boots with fancy spurs. Without exception their lean faces, tanned as leather, wore expressions of impudent recklessness as they escorted the car, still yelling and whooping, right up to the steps of the church.

As Serena alighted from the car they doffed their sombreros in a mocking salute to the shy, uncertain girl who acknowledged their bold appraisal with a nervous nod. Then organ music began thundering from the church and she had no more time to think of nerves as slowly she began walking down the aisle on the arm of Don Alberto towards the tall figure who was waiting, almost unrecognizable in formal dress, his patrician features unnaturally stern.

As if in a dream, Serena played her part to perfection, seeing nothing of the interior of the small, beautifully appointed church, its pews packed with smartly dressed women escorted by proudly erect men, all showing inherent breeding, all descendants of the first band of adventurous *conquistadors* who had made this land their own.

Looking calm and aloof, her slender figure bathed in jewel-coloured sunbeams streaming through a stained glass window, she spoke her vows without a tremor. Inwardly she was numb, ice cold from head to foot, yet terribly conscious of the presence at her side uttering lies with cool deliberation, deceiving every listener with his assurances. *'With my body I thee worship . . .* 'to love and to cherish . . . till death us do part!'

She gave a long shuddering sigh. That, at least, was no lie. It was to be Don Alberto's death that would release them from their bondage – only then would she receive her passport to freedom. That much Juan had promised, and she did not doubt his eagerness to ensure that the promise was kept.

Contact was made once – when Juan slipped the ring upon her finger. His steely hand clasped hers, the long brown fingers wiry and tough as the sharp claws of the condor, the Chilean bird of prey. Momentarily, her eyelids fluttered upwards and she was caught by a gleam of mockery before she hastily looked away.

Only when Don Alberto kissed her did she realize that the dreaded ceremony was over and she relaxed a little, enabled even to cast tentative smiles in the direction of the watching congregation as her bridegroom escorted her back up the aisle. A great cheer broke out when they stepped from the church and she blinked, dazzled by the brilliant sunshine that had replaced the dimness they had left behind. Then a squealing horde of well-wishers descended upon them, showering handfuls of flower petals over her bent head.

With a throaty laugh, Juan urged her towards the car, but her puny strength was no match for the determined women surging for a sight of the bride. So he plucked her from her feet and ran a laughing gauntlet of the *huasos'* womenfolk until he reached the waiting car, his breathless bride still clutched against his heart.

The women were delighted, not only by his action but by the flood of confused colour that had transformed Don Juan's insipid little wife into a creature of shy enchantment.

'Kiss her, *señor*! Kiss her . . . !' they yelled as they were about to gain the sanctuary of the car, and to her horror he complied.

With a jolt that knocked the breath from her body, Serena was set upon her feet. A hard hand grasped her beneath the concealing mantilla, forcing her head still while his mouth lowered to crush her soft lips, drinking in their sweetness like a man thirsting for wine.

When he had drained her dry he thrust her into the car and followed swiftly, closing the door against the madly cheering crowd. As the car moved off, she extricated herself from the bundle of confusion into which she had been tossed and jerked upright, fixing him with a furious stare.

'Such behaviour was not part of our bargain! How dare you treat me like one of the women of the town in which you spend so much of your time!'

His grin faded. With eyes narrowed to slits, he chided, 'Already you sound like a complaining wife, *señora*! And what is this bargain you speak of? I made no bargain, I made a *demand*.'

'You asked me to marry you,' she choked.

'I told you you *would* marry me,' he contradicted coldly. 'Yes, even so, I am willing to admit that as my wife you have some rights. If my visits to town offend you then they shall cease. Anyway, the reason for those visits no longer exists. Marriage has many pains and celibacy has no pleasures, *querida*, so now you are my wife it will be your duty to rid me of the first and alleviate the latter . . .'

CHAPTER SEVEN

THEY stood together near the entrance of the main salon to greet their guests, elegant, well-dressed families seething with curiosity yet too well bred to allow their suspicions any outlet other than discreet whispering amongst themselves and curious glances towards Serena and Juan who, to Serena's surprise, had swooped upon Wendy and commanded Bella:

'Run away and enjoy yourself for an hour, we will look after the child.'

Wendy was delighted and showed her attachment to her favourite man by cooing and gurgling all over him, her tiny fingers caressing his lean brown cheek, her great blue eyes demanding to be shown the attention she yearned. When he responded, it was Serena who gasped, confounded by the transformation caused by a whimsical smile curving lips she had never seen relaxed, eyes which to her had seemed always to pierce with dislike now shining with enjoyment, and a deep-throated chuckle she would have thought impossible from the man whose words bit like a lash.

As Wendy's finger reached out to explore his black, rebelliously groomed hair he laughed aloud and every head turned in their direction just as Don

Alberto entered the salon bearing on his arm the fragile weight of a white-haired old lady whose regal hauteur proclaimed her a matriarch of the same generation as himself. When the murmuring voices hushed Serena tensed, sensing the held breaths and the atmosphere of imminent confrontation.

Leaning heavily on a stick, the old lady stomped forward and as she halted beside them Don Alberto began an introduction, but was waved to silence.

'Already you bear the stamp of domesticity, Don Juan,' she challenged him, her black eyes snapping. 'One could be excused for suspecting the child is yours!'

Serena's cheeks began to burn when an appalled gasp echoed around the room. But Juan's laughing features did not change as he bowed mocking acknowledgment of the outrageous statement.

'It is a matter of regret, Tia Isabella, that many suspicions turn out to be well founded,' he parried, not one whit disturbed. Mindful of their audience, Serena concealed her astonishment. He seemed more pleased than affronted by the old lady's implication, and his reply could not help but foster in the minds of his listeners the suspicion that Wendy was his child and that today's marriage was the act of an honourable man intent upon shouldering his obligations. And then it struck her. Of course! This was his way of redeeming his reputation; far better that he should be scorned as a disreputable rake than be pitied for having to shoulder the burden of another man's child!

Even the sharp-eyed old matriarch was hood-winked.

'Humph . . .!' she regarded him steadily, then her face broke into a smile. 'I apologize, *niño*, I ought to have remembered that it is more shameful to mis-trust one's friends than it is to be deceived by them. Now, introduce me to your bride.'

During the following hours, as they moved amongst their guests chatting lightly, Serena quietly fumed, feeling benevolently tolerated by the haughty, highly-moral company. Juan's words amounting almost to a confession, had broken the ice to such an extent that finally a young, merry-eyed man felt able to jest,

'Small wonder you were so reticent about your absence last year, Juan! A holiday, you said, and nothing more. Defend that statement, if you can, you dog, now that your chickens have come home to roost . . .!'

The dreadful *faux pas* was quickly covered up by the young man's father who began chatting earn-estly to Juan about cattle market prospects. But it was too late; Serena's humiliation was written plainly in scarlet on her fiery cheeks. Murmuring an incoherent excuse, she snatched Wendy from Juan's arms and fled out of the room, leaving an uncomfort-able silence in her wake.

Mercifully, Bella was in the nursery, so Serena handed over the child, then with a thankful sigh retreated into her bedroom feeling drained and exhausted. Tearing the flimsy mantilla from her head, she threw it on to the bed, then sank into a chair in front of her dressing table – to be confronted by humiliation reflecting from the mirror, wounded, enraged eyes, dry yet full of weeping, tears scorched to extinction by heat of temper.

'*Damn him!*' she glared. 'How dared he—'

She flounced from the chair, ripped off her dress and left it lying in a crumpled heap while she slipped into a wrap of cool green cotton. As she plucked the pins from her hair it swept down on to her shoulders, starred and scented by the tiny white blossoms trapped amongst the golden strands. She did not bother to brush them out, but sat before the open window, her bowed head resting upon her arms, struggling with the hatred she felt for the man whom she considered had denuded her of all pride and self-respect.

But she was not to be left in peace much longer. A bare ten minutes had passed when, without a knock of warning, her door was flung open and Juan strode inside, lean as a whip and as startlingly incisive.

'Your absence is beginning to cause comment,' he crisped. 'Get dressed immediately, I'm taking you downstairs.'

The arbitrary command thrust her beyond the bounds of reasons. She jumped to her feet, her body a defiant arc, and berated, 'Indeed you are not ! Your guests can comment as much as they please – heaven knows, they've been supplied with plenty of ammunition – and I refuse to pander further to their well-bred curiosity. I'm staying in my room, so get out and leave me alone!'

He stepped forward to menace with deadly insistence, 'You will do as I say, otherwise I will dress you myself! You have five seconds in which to consider,' he glanced fleetingly at his watch. 'If you have not begun dressing by then you know exactly what to expect.'

Blue eyes stared into brown, blazing defiance against cool implacability. 'I refuse!' she gritted through clenched teeth. 'If you make one move to touch me I shall scream – what will your guests think then?'

'If you scream I shall have to shut you up, using the quickest and most effective means. Make up your mind, time is almost up!'

She felt his will as a barricade of steel, immovable, impenetrable, entirely without mercy. But she discovered within herself an obstinacy she had not known she possessed, a pride that forbade her bending a knee to this tyrant of torment. Besides, although his stance was forbidding she felt certain he would not carry out his threat; no man of breeding could be so brutally ill-mannered. So she tilted her chin and defied him as he stared down at his watch counting off the seconds.

He slicked down his cuff and pounced, the suddenness of his attack taking her completely by surprise. Before she could put up any kind of defence hands like talons clutched the fine cotton wrap and ripped it from neck to hem, whipping it from her shuddering limbs, then throwing it contemptuously into a corner. Her lips parted – not to scream, she was far too shocked, but merely to gasp a shocked protest, but he misconstrued her intention and the hands that had desecrated her wrap descended upon her exposed shoulders and jerked her hard against his tough leanness.

'You must be taught to believe I mean every word I say,' he muttered savagely, then cut off her breath with a kiss punishing enough to drive the lesson home.

Never in her life had Serena suffered such a storm of feeling. It rose rapidly as a tidal bore, sweeping aside sanity, overpowering all power of reason, a devastating inner furore to which she could give no name but which, in her fury, she dubbed hatred.

When Juan judged the lesson had been well learned he lifted his head. 'Well,' he intimidated, 'will you get dressed or shall I . . .?'

From somewhere she found the strength to push him away and mercifully he allowed her to go.

'You fiend!' she shuddered. 'Haven't you humiliated me enough without the added indignity of treating me like a woman of the streets – the sort with whom you are no doubt most familiar!'

'Are you so different from those who haunt the

bars awaiting the *huasos'* pleasure? They, too, sell themselves for money. Some – the hard, brittle creatures – are at least honest, for they make no secret of their aims. But there are others similar to yourself, with sweet, innocent faces, who can make a man feel ashamed of taking what he has bought until he sees them later with yet another man, then he realizes that the sweetness is a façade and they are to be more despised than their more honest sisters!'

She thought she had reached the nadir of shame until he uttered those cruel words, then she realized there was nothing this man would not do to punish her for his resentment. He had promised she would suffer and, as in everything else, his word was his bond!

Shakily, she tried to defend herself. 'I'm not in the least like those women you speak of. When I agreed to come here with your grandfather—'

'He, poor fool, is more easily duped than I,' he cut in. 'He lives in the past century; to him all women require the protection and cosseting of men. It must have been a great shock to you to discover his grandson so much less gullible, so much less receptive to tears, so much more suspicious of feminine wiles. However, *no importa*, we are being impolite to our guests.'

Pointedly he indicated the dress lying crumpled on the floor. 'Put that on and be quick. There is no time for you to arrange your hair, leave it as it is.' A sarcastic grin curved his lips. 'Left loose like that, it will foster the impression that you have been thoroughly kissed.'

Squirming inwardly, Serena began to dress, not from choice but because she had developed a fear of this man with the reckless ways who could not be trusted to react as other men but who was as unpredictable as the wind, as cruel as the sharp-beaked condor.

She expected him to turn his back, but he remained watching her every movement, legs astride, arms folded across his chest, showing not a flicker of sympathy for her embarrassment. Consequently, her fingers fumbled over the tiny buttons and it took her twice as long as usual to don the dress.

Ignoring his decree, she ran a comb quickly through her hair, determined not to appear downstairs as dishevelled as he had suggested, and through the mirror she thought she caught a glimpse of humour in the dark eyes studying her every movement. But she could not be certain and when finally she turned round to face him his expression was noncommittal.

He curled a finger beneath the rope of pearls discarded on the dressing-table and inquired caustically, 'Hadn't you better wear these? Quite a reward for services rendered, they must have cost the old man a packet!'

She despised herself for trembling when, as she fumbled with the clasp, his thumb brushed the nape of her neck. Unchivalrous as ever, he did not allow the incident to pass without comment.

'Heaven help us both if ever I should decide to seduce you,' he frowned. 'In many ways you confound me, not least in the way you retreat like a timid gazelle from my touch. Yet,' he shrugged, 'it is really not surprising, many women of experience are not averse to using naïveté as a blind.'

The first of their guests were saying their goodbyes when they entered the salon. Serena suffered the ritual of speeding their departure in a heat of embarrassment, shaking hands, making polite conversation with faces she saw through a blur of shame, patronizing, supercilious faces, quizzical ones, and the openly pitying. Everyone, it seemed, was relieved that the ordeal was almost over. Some might not have attended had it not been that they valued Don Alberto's friendship more than they abhorred the actions of his wilful grandson. The attitude of many of the older men was strained, in their eyes he had all but disgraced an honourable name, redeeming himself only slightly by a dilatory marriage. Their wives, Serena sensed as she watched them preening complacently over their virginal daughters, were relieved that a menace had been removed from their midst. Don Juan, as everyone knew, was a wild, reckless *hombre*, untamable as a wild-eyed stallion and a law unto himself, as had been proved by his grandfather's inability to impress his authority.

Only the daughters seemed downcast. Subdued, sad-eyed creatures, their freedom restricted by a code of conduct set up centuries earlier, many of them, Serena guessed as they floated past attempting negligent good-byes, would be weeping in their pillows that night, regretting the loss of a man now completely out of their reach.

Doña Isabella was the last to leave – purposely, as was made obvious by the remark she made to Serena when the last of the guests had vanished through the doorway.

'Come, sit by me, my child, I wish to talk to you.' Instinctively, Serena looked to Juan for help, but he shrugged, indicating that there was no escape.

'Not you,' the old lady snapped as he began moving towards her. 'I wish to speak to your wife alone!'

'Very well, Tia, but do not try to gobble her up. She may look sweetly inoffensive, but, like all the English, when cornered she begins to fight.'

'I am pleased to hear it!' Doña Isabella patted a space beside her, directing Serena nearer. 'More mice are caught by traps than by sugar! Your wife will need the strength of Hercules and the wisdom of Solomon if she is to survive marriage to you.'

One wicked black eyebrow shot up. 'And you aim to supply her with such attributes, Tia?'

'There's no need, she is a woman, is she not?' the old lady chided. 'All that is needed is a warning to be on her guard against the bedevilment you have

94

practised from infancy.'

With a short laugh Juan accepted his dismissal and withdrew, leaving Serena alone with the sharp-tongued matriarch whose words had not quite concealed her great fondness for the object of her acid remarks. When the door closed behind him Doña Isabella chuckled.

'He is a charmer, that one! An even greater menace than was his grandfather at the same age. But then I need hardly tell you that, *cara,* you have lassoed the wild one, only do not, I beg you, be tempted to try to make him tame.'

Serena sat silent, her hands clasped in her lap, eyes fixed upon the toe of an elegant shoe peeping from under the hem of Doña Isabella's skirt.

The old lady mused on, seeming unconcerned by her companion's silence, 'I know exactly how you are feeling, for when I was a girl I was madly in love with El Conde. The charm of the Valdivia men is legendary in our community and sprawled across the pages of our history is a trail of broken hearts left by women who had not the sense to realize that men such as these react badly to the whip and only if allowed plenty of slack will they tolerate a hand upon the rein. I was never given a chance to exploit my theory because my father, when he chose my husband, took no heed of the image impressed upon my heart. Then, as now, the Valdivia temperament was frowned upon by fathers who sought conformity rather than charm from prospective sons-in-law. I envy you, *cara*,' she sighed, 'yet I tremble for your youthful innocence. Don Juan did you a great wrong which even today's ceremony cannot completely wipe out. For the sake of your own happiness and his I beg you to be patient with him, turn a deaf ear to his sharp words, reward his frowns with a smile, suffer his temper without fear, and I promise that eventually you will be blessed with a deep and lasting love, and happiness almost too great to bear.'

A smile ghosted across Serena's lips as the old lady stood up to leave. *If only she knew!* So far as she was concerned Don Juan could have rope enough to hang himself. *Please!*

CHAPTER EIGHT

FOR the barbecue that evening Serena chose to wear a gaily-banded evening skirt of many colours topped by a peasant-style blouse with drawstring neckline and full short-length sleeves, of the type favoured by the wives and girl-friends of the *huasos* for whom the party had been especially planned.

She gathered her mane of golden hair into the nape of her neck with a tortoise-shell clasp and shook her head, enjoying the feel of the silken switch that reached almost to her waist. For some reason her spirits began to rise. The prospect of the evening's festivities seemed far less daunting than those that had gone before. The *huasos*, she reflected, unlike Don Alberto's strait-laced contemporaries, would more readily accept her as a friend. Even though they, too, must have been taken aback by the hasty wedding they would not be so quick to condemn and their judgment, though ill-founded, would be more in keeping with their youthful philosophy of living life to the full.

Wendy, tired out by too much petting and fussing, was already asleep when she tiptoed across to the cot before joining Juan and his grandfather downstairs. Already muted sounds of music and laughter could be heard coming from outside and her heart lightened as she tripped downstairs, heading for the small salon where Don Alberto usually enjoyed a drink before dinner. Her smile slipped a little, however, when she entered the room and saw only Juan sprawled out in a chair, twirling a glass of wine between careless fingers.

He rose to his feet when she entered and answered her inquiring look with the dry observation, 'My grandfather, discreet as always, has decided to spend a few days at Doña Isabella's. Thoughtful of him, don't you think?'

Her eyes dilated. 'You mean we've been left alone?'

'Quite alone, except for the servants, whose quarters are some distance from the house,' he quirked. 'So if I should decide to ravish you tonight your screams of protest will go unheard.'

'Don't be ridiculous!' she stammered, mistrusting his taunting smile.

'Don't you be complacent!' he retaliated in a soft drawl, guiding her towards the door outside of which the *huasos* were waiting. 'The night is young, if the evening should progress well who knows what mood you might find me in later?'

Holding herself stiffly beneath his touch, Serena waited for him to step outside, but with his hand upon the latch he swung round to remind her, 'We are, newlyweds, *querida*, and as such will be expected to display some small measure of affection. The bride especially should look starry-eyed and bemused by her good fortune, while I, for my part, will be called upon to show signs of eagerness – to touch you whenever possible, to be seen whispering words of love into your receptive ear and even, when the festivities are at their height, to steal from your inviting lips small sips from the flagon of ecstasy a new husband is privileged to share with his bride. So let us begin with a smile. Wipe the apprehension from your eyes, for after all,' he stressed meaningfully, 'however daunting a prospect may seem it is never quite so bad the second time around!'

The hint of bitterness in his tone was all the fillip she needed. He was sensitive to the *huasos'* opinions, even though aware that, with the speed of light, his lying implications to Doña Isabella would have been fully reported. Well, with his help she was becoming expert in pretence and could support him fully, secure in the knowledge that a screw was being turned on his insufferable pride. So when they stepped outside to shouts of, *Holà! Holà! Mucho gusto, señora!* she was able to smile with so much confidence that even Juan was startled.

The night had a barbaric beauty. Flaming torches had been stuck at intervals in the ground to form a fiery perimeter within which preparations for the feast had begun hours earlier. Above glowing embers young *huasos* were sweating over revolving spits on which whole carcases were slowly roasting. Young girls, their eyes flashing with anticipation, scurried backwards and forwards piling trestle tables with many side dishes: *papas relleans* – potato patties hollowed out and stuffed with chopped meat or cheese and onions, then dipped in beaten egg and fried; maize baked in its husk, and dishes of maize and beans cooked together, topped with eggs poached in beef broth and flavoured with garlic, called, Juan told her, *pancho villa*. He pointed out casks of red and white Chilean wine waiting to be tapped, and pyramids of fruit that held forth a promise of tempting dessert when topped with scoops of *hayskrim*, a delicacy the young *huasos* adored.

Lights strung out beneath the trees were bathing every colour of the spectrum upon glossy leaves when from out of the shadows strolled a group of young men, their swiftly moving fingers plucking sweet music from guitars. With white teeth flashing, they formed a guard of honour for Don Juan and his bride. All chores were forgotten as everyone ran to greet and pay homage to the man they called friend. The prince of cowboys was shortly to become king, but as far as they were concerned tonight was to be his coronation and that of his chosen one, the slim, haunted-eyed girl with whose aloof beauty they themselves would never dream of sharing a bed. But Don Juan was not as other men. He found pleasure in the unique rather than the plentiful and his indifference to the ordinary had been quickly recognized by the women with whom, in the past, he and the *huasos* had shared most of their moments of relaxation.

On the heels of boisterous welcome came a mad scramble for seats when Serena and Juan took their places at the head of a roughly constructed main table. A succulent aroma of roast beef filled the air, as with great flourishes the carving of the carcases began. They ate with their fingers great hunks of beef flavoured with woodsmoke washed down with sharp-tanged wine made from grapes plucked from vines grown in the central valley, as potently breath-taking as the ice-sharp air of the Upper Andes, invisible in the darkness, but in daylight appearing close enough to touch. Laughter and merry companionship gave zest to the meal and even Serena ate well, plunging her small white teeth into portions of beef with the same gusto as her uninhibited companions.

'*Es buena?*' she was asked many times.

To which, to the delight of those around her, she replied: '*Muy fino, señor!*' accompanied by an enthusiastic nod. Word soon began to circulate that La Inglesa, the *Señor bellisima esposa*, had been judged a fitting consort for their king.

After the meal trestles were cleared away and musicians began to play hot, stirring music that had the *huasos* and their womenfolk quickly on their feet.

'The *cueca* is our courtship dance.' Juan leant across to capture Serena's waist when she tried to edge away. 'First of all the woman has to win the interest of the man and then as the dance proceeds she begins to win his heart.'

She barely acknowledged the explanation. Her eyes were fixed upon a dancing couple, both twirling large handkerchiefs above their heads, the girl posturing and pirouetting, inviting the man's attention while his spurs made clink, clink, clink sounds as they knocked together faster, ever faster, in time to the music. All around them spectators were clapping and shouting words of approval and encouragement, then couple after couple began joining in until the arena was full of twirling bodies and stomping feet.

Then from out of the darkness stepped a girl of such tempestuous beauty that Serena's eyes became riveted.

'Gabriela, one of the *mestizos*,' she heard a whisper, quickly shushed, 'one of mixed blood and fiery passions come to seek out her man!'

As if conscious of her unspoken question Juan's quickly indrawn breath supplied an answer. Her suspicion was confirmed a second later when the girl's searching eyes settled upon his face and she began advancing towards him, her fixed stare evidencing that she neither knew nor cared about the scandalized hisses and whispered conjecture of those around her.

With animal grace she paused, then poised on tiptoe in front of him, inviting him to look again upon curvaceous breasts, slim waist and voluptuous thighs, daring him to compare her attributes unfavourably with those of his willow-slim bride. With one insolent flicker of her lashes she dismissed Serena as a pale English ghost, unworthy of the man who had been foolish enough to make her his wife. Serena shivered. Something told her that this girl did not resent being cast aside but regarded the action as a challenge, an opportunity to fight for her man against all odds – and Serena was the first to admit that the odds against her were negligible.

Lazily indulgent, Juan pushed a bowl of fruit towards the girl, inviting her to eat. Her eyes did not leave his face as she reached for an apple and bit crisply into its flesh, then, with the apple impaled on sharp white teeth, she jutted out her chin, inviting him to share it with her in the manner of the first temptress in the garden of Eden. As quickly as Adam, he fell, but when his flashing teeth were within an inch of biting she jerked her head away and stepped back laughing, her eyes taunting him to follow.

The dancers had faltered into a watching circle and with her pretty feet stamping out the rhythm of the music Gabriela backed slowly into the ring, still mutely urging Juan to join her. Without a glance at Serena's expressionless face he strode in pursuit, then, mesmerized by the girl's graceful movement, the watchers began to clap in unison, keeping perfect time with the beat of throbbing guitars. Lance-straight, Juan began stomping, the jingling of his spurs inciting the girl to almost abandoned movements. With her eyes fixed upon his face she circled him slowly, wriggling her hips so that her full skirt billowed and flounced with every jerk of her body. Her advances at first were slow and voluptuous, but as the music quickened so did her steps, and her posturing became wilder and more intense, parading every seductive curve of her body before Juan's unreadable stare.

The tempo increased and she became a banner to his whip, encircling, curling, billowing around his erect leanness, close yet never touching, the yearning in her supple limbs emblazoned for all to see. If this is the beginning of the courtship dance how on earth will it end? Serena wondered. The girl's message was blatantly shocking; obviously she was infatuated with Juan, savagely attracted to the man whose cool detachment had driven her to seek him out even on the day of his wedding. Serena felt creeping embarrassment tinged with pity for the girl who, however much misled, would never have been admitted to the feudal, ruthlessly proud Valdivia household. That she was madly in love was obvious, but that Juan was not was equally so. As a plaything he had probably found her amusing, as a companion wildly satisfying yet never allowed to become too important. Like his legendary namesake, Don Juan was nothing more than an aristocratic libertine, flitting from flower to flower, draining each one dry before plundering the next. He deserved the same fate, Serena thought bitterly, as the man whose debaucheries had supposedly resulted in his being carried off to Hell!

As she watched he glanced her way and his glint of mockery warned that her thoughts were written plainly on her expressive face. Angry with herself and with him, she waited until his back was turned, then rose quietly and slipped unnoticed into the surrounding darkness. No one saw her go, nevertheless, she began to run until she reached the hacienda where once inside she raced up to her room and banged the door, remaining leaning against its panels until she had regained her breath and subdued some of the inward quivering brought about, she assured herself, by the deep contempt in which she held the man who earlier that evening had threatened to claim the privileges of a husband. With a shudder of revulsion she turned the key in the lock and began to undress. The night was still young by *huasos'* standards, but she felt deathly tired, seeming to have run the gamut of emotions during a never-ending day.

She groped for her nightdress, but it was not where she expected to find it, so, mystified, she pulled open a drawer and found it empty, as was the next drawer and the next. Then when she opened the doors of her wardrobe she found that it too was bare. A shiver of panic drove her across to the bed where she flung back the top cover and discovered it had been stripped to the mattress – sheets, pillows, clothes, all had disappeared.

At the sound of hard footsteps advancing up the

stairs she threw the silk bedcover hastily around her shivering limbs and stood petrified when the footsteps halted outside her door. When the doorknob was vigorously rattled she remained silent, then Juan's voice grated its way through the woodwork.

'Let me in, *esposa*, unless you want me to break down the door!'

He had no need to threaten, she knew he intended exactly what he said; if she did not comply he would not hesitate to startle Wendy from her sleep.

It was hard to appear dignified clad only in a thin silken sheet, but she strove to look unconcerned when he sauntered inside, taking in the evidence of her search with one sweeping glance.

'You surely did not expect to occupy this solitary little room once we were married?' he mocked, back-healing a gaping wardrobe door shut. 'Carmen's romantic soul would shrivel at the thought! It was she who moved your things into the room we are to share.'

She reeled at the implication. 'What do you mean? You never said . . . I never imagined . . .'

'Then don't begin now!' he laughed. 'We are to occupy two adjoining rooms. One, which is intended as my dressing-room, contains a bed which I shall use; as I am an early riser I shall have ample time in which to rid it of all signs of occupation before the servants' suspicions are aroused. We would be wise, I think, to allow them to find us together in your bedroom on two or three occasions, or is that too much to ask, my puritanical little prude?'

Serena could not deny the logic of his argument. After all, the whole point of this morning's ceremony was to pull the wool over the eyes of the Señor and the aim of the exercise would be put at risk were servants' gossip ever to reach his ears. 'Very well,' she conceded unhappily, 'then will you please show me to the room I'm to occupy. I'm c-cold . . .'

Juan responded by scooping her up into his arms and striding out into the passageway. She dared not wriggle as he descended the stairs heading towards the main bedroom on the floor below; through the silken sheet his hands felt like branding irons against her skin. Aware of her tenseness, he laughed, his daredevil eyes raking her confused loveliness.

'Tell me,' he murmured as he halted outside the bedroom door, 'why did you run away? Afraid of the competition, or were you perhaps a little jealous?'

'Jealous?' Serena echoed blankly. 'Of *you* . . .'

Her incredulous inflection set an edge upon his smile and without another word he strode into the bedroom and set her down upon her feet. As she slithered from his arms the silk cover slipped, leaving her shoulders bare, and she clutched feverishly at the material, half expecting to see scorch marks where his hands had touched.

Nervously she braved his sombre gaze, wondering what form of devilment his silence was about to precede.

'No!' he surprised her, 'jealousy is too fiery an emotion to be experienced by an iceberg such as yourself! What *are* your feelings beneath that glacial exterior? *Do* you feel? *Can* you feel? It might be interesting to find out!'

She could not defend herself against the arms that reached out to jerk her forward against his hard chest, her hands were fully occupied keeping in place the flimsy covering that was threatening to slip from her body if her grasp should slacken. So she was gathered against him with hands clasped tightly in front of her and her attempts to evade his lowering head merely added to his humourless amusement.

Hampered as she was, his hands were left free to roam. And they did, hatefully, intimately over every silk-covered curve. Intense heat seared her even though outwardly she forced herself to appear calmly contemptuous while he practised the art of seduction with a skill that left her in no doubt of his ability.

'Relax, *cara*,' he wooed, his lips exploring a bare shoulder, tracing a trail of burning kisses along her slender arched neck, then hovering, his lips fractionally from her ear. He whispered a strong Spanish imprecation that sounded more frustrated than desirous, then, impatient with her lack of response, he stroked his lips across her cheek until he found her mouth, assaulting its tender sweetness until the churning inside her erupted into a white-hot blaze so consuming she became intensely afraid.

When he lifted his head she saw satisfaction so aggravating she lost control and without stopping to think lifted her hand to deliver a stinging blow across his cheek. As she withdrew her hand his fingers snapped around her wrist, then holding it captive he grasped her other hand and squeezed hard to force her into releasing her hold upon the flimsy covering.

A red mist of pain swam before her eyes as she resisted increased pressure. She held on as long as she could, but his strength was all-powerful and after a particularly vicious jab she uttered a moan and the material slipped through her crushed fingers.

She had imagined the extent of her hatred had been fully reached until he laughed. At that moment, given the strength, she would gladly have killed him!

'So, the iceberg burns!' he taunted softly. 'All that was needed was a spark from the right kind of man!'

Immobile as an alabaster statue, feeling stripped in soul as well as body, she condemned through a tear-tight throat, 'You are not a man, you are a beast, and I hate you!'

She braced herself for further humiliating laughter, but his answer was low and intense. 'At least I make you feel passionately – more passionately, I'm willing to bet, than the child's father ever did!'

In the midst of degradation the reminder of her father came as the cruellest blow of all. Her heart swelled to bursting point as she struggled to stem heartbroken tears, but as the first of them escaped her downcast lashes she heard Juan's indrawn breath, then his sharp, incredulous question.

'You weep for the man who deserted you? You feel for him still?'

'He did not desert me, he died,' she denied brokenly. 'And of course I love him — I always will ...'

After silent, drawn-out seconds he stooped to retrieve the silken heap from the floor. Gently he draped it around her shivering body, swaddling her like a baby, then he lifted her into his arms and strode across to deposit her on the bed.

Suspecting further torment, she swept her tear-wet lashes upwards, but he was standing erect and motionless, his dark eyes full of brooding disquiet.

'Rest easily, *querida*, I have no wish to compete with the stealthy wooing of the dead. But think on this — You are involved in mankind, and while you exist you must tolerate the weaknesses of those who compare unfavourably with those whose virtues are indestructible only because they are no longer alive to err. Forget him, *cara*, let him rest in peace, for a man who is not forgotten is not dead.'

CHAPTER NINE

DURING the following weeks life fell into a pattern more peaceful than Serena had ever dared hope. After returning from his short stay at Doña Isabella's Don Alberto was confounded by Juan's adamant refusal to take over the running of the hacienda – the aim he had schemed to achieve – and his insistence upon continuing working as usual with the *huasos* on duties that entailed his leaving the hacienda every morning before sunrise to ride the miles of pampas stretching farther than the eye could see, sorting, branding and rounding up strays from the immense herds Serena remembered as a heaving mass of brown carpeting the floor of a lush valley.

At times he was absent for many days, driving the cattle to a distant port for shipping, and arriving back at the hacienda looking tired and covered in dust, seeming taller than ever astride a saddle under which many thick blankets had been placed to make the ride more comfortable for both man and beast.

But finally, after one of Juan's long absences, Don Alberto rebelled. He was sunbathing at the side of the pool, finding great amusement in the antics of Wendy who, from the safety of Serena's arms, was reacting with screams of joy and terror to her first initiation into the pool. Sun, hot yet not fierce, was setting thousands of sparkles a-shimmer on the water reflecting the cool deep green of submerged tiles. A brief white swimsuit contrasted perfectly against Serena's newly-acquired tan and its figure-hugging lines drew attention to a fullness that had superseded the angularity of her once undernourished body. Her trill of happy laughter rang out as Wendy, panicking from the depth of water, grabbed her mane of golden hair and began climbing out of reach of the lapping water.

To the travel-weary man who strode into their midst the scene was as welcome as a mirage in the desert, a sight so gratifying he could barely tear his eyes away. Then Don Alberto looked up and saw him.

'Juan, my boy, welcome home! Look, Serena, here is Juan. Come, show him how happy you are to have him back!'

Under the pretence of disengaging Wendy's fist from her hair, she hid her confusion. She knew what the old gentleman expected of her and so, too, did Juan, as she saw by the flicker of mockery lurking deep in his dust-rimmed eyes. Her heart gave an unexpected leap as slowly she advanced towards him, using Wendy as a shield between herself and the saddle-weary man in whose absence she had gloried, discovering within the confines of the hacienda a peace which as each day passed seemed set to grow into happiness.

Dutifully, beneath Don Alberto's benevolent stare, she lifted up her face, shrinking inwardly from the anticipated kiss, then felt almost slighted when Juan's lips brushed fractionally across her cheek before he lifted his head to concentrate his attention upon Wendy.

'And how is my *bellisima* today?' He lifted the wildly wriggling infant into his arms. 'Much as I would like to play with you, *chiquita*, I am too hot and dusty. Here, I will hand you back to Mamaita while I have a quick shower.'

'Why not join us after in the pool?' Serena's shocked ears could barely believe that her own lips had formed the words.

Narrowly he eyed her across the top of Wendy's head. 'Very well,' he accepted, 'if that is your wish.'

His grandfather beamed, 'But of course it is her wish! For a very new wife, Serena has accepted her neglect well, but I have decided there are to be no more of these prolonged absences. After dinner you and I will discuss your new role as head of the *hacienda*. Seventy long years are enough, I have made up my mind to abdicate and will not delay a moment longer! However, have your shower, then enjoy your swim. You and Serena must have much to talk about, so our discussion can wait until later. But remember this, I do not intend to listen to any further arguments from you about wanting time to get whatever is bothering you out of your system, you have had time enough and to spare!'

Juan sent his grandfather a brief nod and with-drew to do as he had been bid.

At last, Serena reflected while she awaited his return, he was about to be handed all that he had striven to achieve. For this very outcome he had entered into a marriage that entailed years of lost freedom; small wonder he had insisted upon a breathing space, a few weeks' grace in which to say a lingering good-bye to the life he loved, to his friends, the *huasos*, and to Gabriela . . .

Deep in thought, she did not notice Don Alberto signalling Bella to take Wendy indoors, nor did she notice his own quiet exit when Juan strode back into view, his muscular virility displayed to advantage by black briefs, a towel slung across his shoulders soak-ing up the moisture left by his shower.

'You invited me to swim with you,' he startled her by saying. 'Does the invitation still stand or was it offered purely as a sop to my grandfather?'

Serena caught her breath, able at that moment to understand the magnetism that kept women welded to his side. He was too physically perfect for his own good, muscles rippling like silk beneath skin tanned to the brown of leather. He coiled his whip-slim leanness to peer into her face. 'Well?' he quirked.

Suddenly she wanted to join him. 'All right, I'd love to!'

With the aid of the arm he obligingly held out, she levered herself upward, then very conscious of the briefness of her swimsuit she ran the length of the pool before diving in, cutting the water cleanly as a knife. Exhilaration coursed through her veins when Juan's shadow loomed by her side, powerful strokes skimming him through the water at a speed far outreaching her own.

He was waiting for her when she reached the far end, floating on a cushion of green water with his eyes lifted heavenwards, wearing the expression of a man who had just reached the ultimate of immediate ambition.

'I've dreamt of this moment for days,' he murmured, cocking her a sideways glance. 'This last drive was more than usually fraught with mishaps and delays, the cattle fractious with heat, the men only slightly less so . . .'

'No doubt there were compensations once you reached civilization.' The dryness in her tone would not be suppressed.

He rolled over. 'Some!' he supplied crisply, then dived beneath the surface, grabbing her ankles so that she was forced down with him to the bottom of the pool. Her lungs felt ready for bursting by the time he released her and she shot up to the surface, gasping for breath. When his head bobbed up beside her she retaliated immediately and a game began. For an hour they frolicked in the manner of children, completely natural and carefree, their differences submerged by an unexpected accord that was unbelievably precious because each was aware of the obstacles that destined it could not last.

They stretched out on sun loungers and Carmen brought them long cool glasses of *limonada* to sip while they dried in the sun.

'I love your summers,' Serena sighed, 'so dry yet never unpleasantly hot. I can hardly believe it's January; in London it will probably be snowing, the pavements covered in slush and everyone bad-temperedly pushing and shoving their way on to buses, complaining bitterly about the weather.'

She had caught Juan's interest. Lazily he eyed her. 'Tell me about yourself,' he asked abruptly, 'how you existed before you met my grandfather — *how* you met my grandfather.'

Her contented expression faded; for once while in his company she had been feeling relaxed, but the question pushed her once more on to dangerous ground.

'I worked in an office,' she stammered, 'and Wendy and I shared a small bedsitter nearby.'

'What happened to the child while you were at work?'

'I left her at a nursery each morning and picked her up each night on my way home.'

Her few weeks at the hacienda had given her sufficient insight into the Spanish way of life to know that he would find this admission shocking. The Chileans were a race who doted on their children and insisted upon a mother's constant attention.

'I had no alternative,' she defended. 'Anyway, in

my country it's the accepted thing for working mothers to leave their children in the care of nurseries which are very strictly supervised by the authorities.'

His dark eyes sparkled. 'And you consider officialdom a suitable substitute for mother love?'

Suddenly his catechism angered her. 'No, I don't, that's the reason I'm here! I was desperately worried about Wendy's wellbeing, but when the nursery fees were raised I couldn't afford to keep her there anyway. Then my landlady told me I had to leave because Wendy's crying was disturbing the other residents, and that was the final straw. Circumstances drove me into answering your grandfather's advertisement—' She broke off, wondering just how much Juan knew of his grandfather's methods, and suffered an uneasy qualm when his limbs stiffened.

'Yes, do go on about my grandfather's advertisement,' he drawled dangerously. 'How exactly was it worded?'

Serena wanted to jump up and run, but his look held her manacled until she was forced to repeat the words stamped indelibly on her mind. 'English girl required for post demanding absolute and total commitment in return for,' she gulped, 'lifelong security and freedom from want. Must be of discreet, docile disposition.' She winced when he uttered a hard laugh, then stumbled on, 'Preferably of fair complexion,' then, her voice descending to a whisper, 'dependants welcome.'

'*Madre mia!*' he hissed, 'you risked walking into the jaws of hell! Why did no one warn you of the dangers?'

'No one knew,' she replied with dignity. 'Wendy and I are completely devoid of relatives and as I have already said, I was desperate enough to do *anything* that would enable us to stay together.'

Juan swung upright and glowered. 'Obviously,' his steely jaw jutted, 'if my grandfather had insisted upon your marrying the devil himself you would not have turned him down!'

How can I deny it? she thought wildly, petrified by his satanical expression. Yet for some unknown reason she tried.

'No, no,' she all but pleaded, 'your grandfather tricked me – not with outright lies but by allowing me to form a completely erroneous impression of the grandson he wanted me to marry. He implied that you were too shy and diffident to find a wife for yourself and that his actions were being carried out with your full approval. I would never have come had I known how resentful you felt and how totally different you were from the image I had conceived!'

He muttered an imprecation against his grandfather's duplicity, but his glance was no kinder as he roved her distressed features. 'So you came to Chile expecting to find a dove and instead had your sensitivities ripped apart by a sharp-clawed condor? My grandfather wronged us both and in time we will have our revenge, but meanwhile I shall see to it that your reward is sufficiently increased to compensate for your sacrificial gesture?'

As he stood up to stalk away, Serena protested, 'Your grandfather has already been more than generous, I want nothing more—'

A haughty gesture silenced her. 'A paltry sum spent on clothing and a roof over your head cannot be classed as riches, yet if he had showered you with wealth you would still, to my mind, be left with nothing!'

Five minutes after he had gone she dragged herself up to her room. The sun was still warm but she felt chilled by his blast of contempt. It was nothing new, this duel of personalities, from the first moment of meeting they had crossed swords and, as usual, she was the one to retire bearing the worst scars. But this time Juan's rapier tongue had penetrated deeper, probably because during their hour-long truce she had been foolish enough to shed the armour she always wore in his company.

As she shed her swimsuit she heard sounds of movement coming from his dressing-room. Since the night of their wedding he had not ventured into her bedroom, even though an unlocked door was the only barrier between them. This was the room his parents had shared, the ill-fated couple whose marriage had begun as theirs had begun but which, according to Don Alberto, had developed into a blaze of love. She closed her eyes, striving to sense the atmosphere of happiness that must surely linger in this room above all others had their love been as great as Don Alberto had said. But she felt nothing.

Could it be, she wondered, that history had, indeed, repeated itself? Had Juan's parents been equally successful in hiding from the old gentleman the true situation that had existed? As she slipped into a wrap she pondered. But what of Juan? Was he not living proof of their love? Sudden heat scorched her body, reminding her of the tempestuous passions passed down from fathers to sons. Her eyes strayed to the unlocked door, fearfully conscious that should Juan ever decide to carry out his threat the absence of love would not deter him.

A couple of hours had to elapse before it would be time to begin dressing for dinner, so she stretched out on the bed, physically weary yet too agitated to sleep. Her eyes roved the interior of the *dormitorio de matrimonio*, decorated almost completely in virginal white. Carefully folded at the foot of her bed was a crocheted spread of purest white wool edged with a foot-long silken fringe. The headboard was of white enamel ornamented with golden scrolls and matching table lamps with shades edged in gold cast soft pools of colour upon pale blue walls, bare except for one muted colour print and a large gilt-framed mirror. Curtains of heavy white satin fringed with blue were held apart from windows reaching from floor to ceiling, by tasselled cords. Fitted wardrobes enamelled white lent added spaciousness, as did the pure white carpet scattered with tiny golden flowers leafed in green that flowed luxuriously into each corner of the room.

'*Romantica . . .*' she murmured drowsily. Then her heavy eyelids drooped under a weight of weariness.

An hour later she woke refreshed and after a shower felt completely revitalized. To match her cheerful mood she chose a dress of poppy red, backless, strapless, and with a daring cleavage – a banner of defiance with which to bolster her timidity. She sought a matching lipstick and hid her sensitive mouth beneath a slash of poppy red, then she held large hooped earrings against her cheek. Pleased with the effect, she slipped them into her lobes and swung her head from side to side, adapting to the unfamiliar weight.

She was poised before a full-length mirror when Juan walked in, his footsteps muffled by the thick carpet. She sensed his presence and swung round, indignation replacing pleasure. Then just as she was about to reproach him she was silenced by a narrow-eyed stare that began tracing every outline so tightly bound by the red sheath that the unbared was more provocatively revealed than the bared. Flattered by his stunned silence, she preened a little, then jerked with shock when his distasteful voice directed,

'Take off that dress!'

She shied as if bitten, then tilted her chin. 'Why? I think it suits me!'

'As the hide of a puma would suit a lamb!' he spat. 'It is the dress of a woman of seduction, and you, *cara*, have not the faintest idea how to seduce.' He reached out, swiftly hooked the large earrings into the crook of his finger and flung them into a far corner. Then he caught her by the shoulder and held her steady while one cruel hand wiped across her mouth, smearing a trail of poppy red across her cheek. 'Now wash your face and dispose of that dress,' he commanded. 'It is indecent!'

Furiously Serena rounded on him. 'What do you know of decency? Did you think of decency when you allowed Gabriela to make her blatant advances, proving to everyone with eyes that it was she you ought to have married?'

'Leave Gabriela out of this!' he cut in, his lips compressing.

'Ah, so you do have a conscience!' she tilted.

'Yes, I have a conscience,' he surprised her, by saying, slipping a hand into the pocket of his dinner jacket and withdrawing a flat, velvet-covered case. 'If any of our *huasos* were underpaid I should feel they were being exploited, and you are every bit as entitled to consideration. These belonged to my mother. I have brought them for you as added payment for your services. Wear them this evening.' He snapped open the case to reveal a necklace of sapphires which, as the light fell upon them, seemed to pulsate into life.

Serena blanched from the insult, but stood her ground.

'No, thank you, they won't go with my dress.'

She should have known better. A second later she was spun like a top in his hands, there came the rasp of a zip, then a harsh ripping sound as he took the dress between his hands and tore it to the hem.

'That problem is now solved,' he stated grimly. 'To save future argument, to say nothing of protecting the contents of your wardrobe, kindly remember that I am used to having my orders promptly obeyed.' Calmly he consulted his watch. 'You have ten minutes to spare before dinner – ample time in which to decide upon a suitable alternative.'

CHAPTER TEN

DINNER was a strained affair. Only Juan was unperturbed, chatting his way through the courses, ignoring Serena's set features and endeavouring to hold his grandfather's interest so that he, too, would do the same. But Don Alberto's eyes would not be diverted from her wan, unhappy face.

She was conscious of his anxiety, yet could not pretend an interest in food when every mouthful was having to pass through lips uncontrollably trembling before forcing a way past a constriction in her throat. She had been shocked to the core by Juan's brutal insistence upon having his way, even to the extent of standing grim guard while she had fumbled her way into the dress she was now wearing – a plain cream shift she had grabbed without thought from her wardrobe, a simple foil for the sapphires sparkling icy blue above her frozen heart.

Don Alberto frowned. 'I have been thinking,' he addressed Juan, but his eyes traced Serena's downcast face, 'before you take over the running of the hacienda it might be a good idea if you both have a holiday – a belated honeymoon,' he carried on doggedly, undeterred by their lack of enthusiasm. 'A couple of weeks at the coast would be nice; I had intended making a prolonged visit to relatives in Spain, but that can wait until your return. You will love our summer playground, Serena, the Viña del Mar has wonderful beaches and fine hotels – even a gambling casino that attracts visitors from all over the world.'

Feeling confident that Juan would not agree, she was rendered speechless when he replied, 'The prospect certainly has appeal. A visit to the coast might also benefit the child.'

But on this issue Don Alberto stood firm. 'A honeymoon is for two,' he insisted. 'Wendy will remain here with us.'

Serena's lips parted, but Juan intercepted her protest. 'Perhaps you are right. It is decided, then, we will leave for Viña del Mar early tomorrow morning.'

Happily reassured, his grandfather left them alone as soon as dinner was over. It was a hot, sultry evening and the breeze drifting through open windows did nothing to alleviate the stifling atmosphere that descended like a cloak immediately he made his exit.

'Would you care to walk in the grounds?' Juan suggested, indifferent to the point of boredom.

Serena was about to refuse, but then deciding anything was preferable to spending hours cooped up indoors, she nodded agreement.

'I'll fetch you a wrap.' He rose to his feet as if welcoming the prospect of any activity, however slight, and returned after a few moments carrying a shawl of heavily embroidered silk. 'This ought to do,' he approached, 'substantial yet light.'

She shied from his touch and grasped the ends of the shawl he placed around her shoulders in tightly clenched fists.

'Don't worry,' he interpreted her action correctly, 'I have no intention of ripping up every article you possess, only those items which offend.'

'I find it strange that a man who prefers his amours to be flamboyant should insist upon an aura of chastity surrounding his wife,' she retorted scathingly, his barbaric action still rankling.

Juan considered her thoughtfully. 'We have a proverb, *chica*, that states: "The only chaste woman is one who has not been asked." Surely the presence of the child testifies quite plainly that such a sentiment cannot be applied to you?'

She swept past him, avoiding the caustic glance that would have recognized immediately the glimmer of tears, and felt fiercely glad that she had this one weapon with which to torment his pride. If she used it well, in time he might find her presence insufferable and be only too willing to refund her passage home.

Bathed in moonlight bright as day, they wandered into the beautiful, almost tropical garden attached to the house surrounded by eucalyptus trees positioned purposely to screen from sight a spread of buildings, covering ground sufficient to have accommodated several city blocks, built some distance away from the hacienda. The bulk was made up of granaries, store-rooms, workshops, implement sheds, dairy barns, a silo or two, stables for saddle horses and, not far away, numerous small dwellings strung along both sides of the main hacienda road like a village within a single street a conglomeration of workers and their families all dependent for their existence upon the hacienda.

'A feudal type of slavery,' she muttered under her breath, 'with the happiness of each individual dependent upon the whim of one man.'

Unaware of the direction of her thoughts, Juan began idly explaining, 'When this region was newly conquered by our armies, one of the first acts of the Spanish crown was to reward the officers of the army by granting them *encomiendas*. These were not grants of land but only grants of the right to collect tribute from certain Indian communities. But then the desire to own land became so strong a motivating force that the ownership of an *encomienda* did not satisfy, so outright grants of land were then sought from the crown. These grants were made, varied in size according to the position and merit of the person – town lots for those who wished to live in the town; small farms for soldiers of low rank, and vast estates measured in square leagues for the officers of high rank.

'That is how we Valdivias became owners of this hacienda and assumed our position in accordance with the traditions of our society. It works well, the *huasos* look upon us not merely as employers but as the head of a large family, each man following in the footsteps of his ancestors who worked here centuries previously, and being conditioned from birth to regarding the head of the Valdivia family as his *patrón*.'

'Or as a patriarch living in a world apart!' she retorted, rallying to the cause of those who, like herself, had no option but to accept the rulings of a dictator. 'You pride yourself that workers are not permitted to starve, yet no pressure of opinion exists which forces you to raise their standard of living above the bare necessities which tradition has accorded is all they deserve! I have no doubt that, although held to the estate on which he was born only by custom, any *huaso* would find it difficult – no, impossible – to find employment elsewhere if he should attempt to leave!'

Drawing proudly erect, he hissed, 'Our workers are free to go when and wherever they wish!'

'As free as I am?' she taunted. 'You know quite well that other hacienda owners would not employ them; only in the city would they be able to find work. You Valdivias are despots, you use people as if they were puppets instead of flesh and blood, manipulating, manoeuvring, forcing them against their will to do whatever you wish, regardless of their own desires – take this holiday, for instance, you know I have no wish to go to the coast, and especially not with you!'

While she had been pouring out her resentment Juan had looked fierce, but at her final outburst his scowl cleared and an almost teasing light flashed into his eyes.

'Is the prospect of a few days in my company so daunting?' he clipped. 'You need a holiday, *chiquita*, you are looking drawn and tense, you need to relax in an atmosphere of carefree abandon such as you will find at Viña del Mar. But besides that,' his voice hardened, 'my grandfather's mood must be kept mellow. Success is almost within my grasp, and if a holiday together is all that is needed to obtain a kingdom then a holiday we shall have. In this respect you are right, I will allow nothing to stand in the way of my plans. Yet as I am feeling more benevolently disposed towards you I will promise that you need have no qualms about accompanying me to Viña del Mar – indeed, I will do everything in my power to ensure that you enjoy the break which need not be fraught with strife. With your co-operation I will make it a holiday to remember – a bonus payment for the services you have so ably rendered.'

They set off the next morning, the plane, with Juan at the controls, rising like a bird into the blue sky, circling the hacienda once to dip wings in a final salute before heading west in the direction of the coast. Sitting in the cockpit next to Juan was an experience that could have been frightening were it not for the fact that whatever her opinion of him as a man she had utmost confidence in the assured brown hands manipulating the controls. But it was hard to relax as the plane rose higher and higher until the ground was barely visible beneath them.

Wearing lightweight slacks and an open-necked shirt, he looked carefree, seeming determined to enjoy the unexpected break, with or without his companion's co-operation.

He stole a sideways glance at the slight figure sitting tensely erect, her clasped hands resting in her lap, wearing an expression of mingled excitement and trepidation.

'Would you care for a turn at the controls?' he amazed her by asking.

Serena shrank visibly from the prospect. 'No, thank you,' she stammered, sensing the devilment in him. During her first flight with Don Alberto she had felt no fear, not even when stepping into the smaller private plane had she experienced a qualm, but on neither occasion had the pilot had eyes dancing with mischief, nor the devil-may-care expression of a man released from the shackles of responsibility and intent upon cramming as much enjoyment as possible into his short, unexpected holiday.

He depressed a lever and the nose of the plane lifted until they were climbing vertically into the heavens. Serena's slight body felt crushed by an invisible force against the back of her seat. Blood pounded in her ears, and breath was cut off at her throat, making it impossible to speak. Juan levelled out and for a bare second she relaxed, then he headed the plane into a spin that sent them diving madly to earth at such speed she was sure disaster must be inevitable. She closed her eyes and clenched her chattering teeth, braced for impact, then as her lips moved soundlessly in prayer she felt the plane curve and the screaming engines subside into a comforting throb.

She opened her eyes and could have scratched the laughter from his grinning face. 'You fool,' she choked, 'we could have been killed!'

He laughed aloud. 'But what a way to go, *chica,* blazing a swift, clean trail of defiance!'

She gathered her scattered wits. 'Go if you must, *señor,* but go alone. Personally I would prefer to live in misery than die in glory.'

The rest of the flight was completed peaceable and in comparative silence until the plane began losing height, preparatory to landing. Below was Valparaiso.

'Do you wonder we call it Valley of Paradise?' Juan nodded downward.

Serena craned forward to look down upon a city curved like a sickle around a harbour packed with ships and just had time to see the dipping of powerful cranes loading and unloading cargo before they began circling the airfield.

To her disappointment, the taxi Juan hired sped

straight through Valparaiso. She would have liked to linger in the city built in big steps on rocky hills rising out of a bay. 'The town is built on two levels,' he informed her, 'and is divided into an upper and a lower town. The lower, hugging the waterfront, is the business part and the upper is residential. The two are connected by *ascensores* – lifts, hauled by strong cables in a slanting line.'

After a fifteen-minute drive northward along the shore from Valparaiso they came to Viña del Mar, and Serena was immediately enchanted by a stretch of smooth white sand dotted with gay umbrellas, and *cabañas* splashing the bathing beaches with bright colours. Above the beaches quaint horse-drawn carriages clip-clopped along past old mansions and new homes. Stately palms and pines lined well paved streets and everywhere there were flowers.

'Such a riot of scent and colour!' she exclaimed, her eyes widening with delight.

'It is a town law that every resident with room for flowers *must* grow them,' Juan smiled, his hand reaching for the inner door handle as their taxi drew up in front of an imposing hotel.

In a dream state she followed him through the foyer, then they were whisked upwards in a lift to the very pinnacle of the building before being conducted into a penthouse suite, an eyrie of luxury, decorated in the colours of springtime, with huge picture windows framing a view of the restless blue

Pacific.

'It pleases you?' Juan came up behind her as she stood gazing rapturously out of the window.

'It's breathtaking!' She spun round with a smile of pure pleasure, her wide eyes retaining in their depths some of the sparkling blue of the ocean.

She caught him off guard. Used to encountering suspicion and underlying hostility, he seemed at a loss to know how to cope with her uninhibited pleasure. He stared for so long she became self-conscious, her smile giving way to a confused blush. Something about that stare warned her to remain offhand and wary of this man of moods who seemed at present to be straining against a leash, a creature of dangerous, erratic impulses.

When nervously she edged away he drawled, 'I am willing to forget that you are a woman if you will try to forget that I am a man. I am weary of this battle of the sexes. Why don't we lay down our arms and agree to an uncomplicated truce for the duration of our stay?'

Forget that he was a man! He was asking the impossible! Yet she nodded agreement, crossing her fingers to cancel out the lie.

'Good!' His smile rocked her on her heels. 'Then as we have agreed to be playmates, let's freshen up before finding out what the town has to offer.'

Their adjoining rooms had a bathroom between which he allowed her to occupy first, and as she slipped into a white dress, banded around the neckline and sleeves with crisp gingham, Serena heard his unmelodious voice rising above the splash of the shower.

Her hands shook as she pinned her cloud of golden hair into a clip. With excitement? With fear? With *anticipation*, she reluctantly admitted, admonishing her rising spirits with a reminder to beware of the Spaniard bearing gifts.

But the warning was forgotten when Juan strolled into her room, handsome as the devil in black slacks and a matching tee-shirt that clung like a second skin to his flexing muscles.

'Are you ready?' He held out his hand, glinting approval of her appearance, and she slipped her fingers into his, feeling for the first time for many months a surge of youthful happiness.

For the first hour they strolled along the seafront soaking up the atmosphere of gaiety emanating from the sunbathing, pleasure-loving crowds thronging the beaches. Juan bought her *hayskrim* and seafood dredged only hours earlier from the floor of the ocean, unheeding of her laughing protest that she would spoil her appetite for dinner. They sat on a wall watching the rise and fall of boats moored in the small harbour, laughed at the antics of gulls diving for scraps, then sauntered arm in arm back to the hotel, engrossed in conversation, oblivious of interested onlookers who had labelled them lovers.

Feeling sticky, hot and happy, Serena entered the

drawing-room attached to their suite. As Juan busied himself pouring out drinks she felt an impulse to thank him.

'Today has been fun.' Her skirt billowed as she sank down on to the settee. 'I much prefer having you as a friend rather than a husband.'

His face was enigmatic as he offered her a drink before tossing back his own, the muscles of his throat moving silken-smooth with every swallow.

When he set down the empty glass she eyed it doubtfully. Everything he did was done with vigour, even his drinking! She knew him to be self-willed and devious – was she being foolish to take his words at face value? Was his change of attitude a ploy to lull her into a false sense of security? He was a virile, full-blooded man and he had not seen Gabriela for quite some time . . .!

He caught her eyes and smiled, a completely guileless smile. 'Friendship is a slow-ripening fruit, niña. Ours is like a new wine, when it ages we will drink it with pleasure.'

Momentarily disarmed, Serena smiled back and took the hand he extended to heave her from her seat. 'Time to dress for dinner,' he indicated with a nod the darkening sky outside of their window. 'We will dine early, amiga, then we will go and search out the maximum of pleasure from this valley of paradise.'

CHAPTER ELEVEN

SERENA had no idea what she ate for dinner that evening – ambrosia, she might have guessed if asked, washed down with nectar served in silver goblets by woodland nymphs. They sat close together at a table for two, so deeply absorbed they were unaware of other diners – women envious of her superbly handsome escort and men coveting the dewy-eyed innocence of his companion.

'Tell me about your early life,' Juan encouraged. 'Were you happy as a child?'

'Very happy.' His glance was caught and held by the soft glow in her eyes. 'My parents were wonderful people,' she reminisced, 'and I suppose they spoiled me dreadfully, but I was their only child, at least until—' She stopped abruptly, a tide of colour suffusing her cheeks.

'Yes, until . . . ?' His eyebrows drew together in puzzlement.

'Until . . . they died,' she stammered.

'They died together as mine did?' he queried, sympathy in his tone.

'Not exactly . . . but within six months of each other.'

'I'm sorry if the subject is still painful, perhaps I ought not to have asked. It is just that I somehow sense that you have not always been so coolly distant. I wish we could have met before life had time to scar your youthful charm. Wendy's father – did your parents approve of him? Mothers are notoriously quick to protect their young – did yours look upon him as a suitable husband?'

Her blush deepened as, feeling indescribably deceitful, she answered truthfully, 'My mother adored him.'

'Ah!' Thoughtfully he paused before questioning further. 'And how do you think she would have regarded me?'

Serena had often asked herself that very question without finding a satisfactory answer. He was so completely outside their ken that her mother, she felt sure, would have regarded him with as much awe as she did herself. She had berated the Valdivias for their arbitrary manner, yet she had to admit that they were unique, as far removed from the commonplace as the stars glittering overhead.

Impatiently Juan awaited her answer. She breathed in deeply. 'My mother was as susceptible as most women to charm, as admiring of good looks, and as yielding to flattery, but . . .'

'Yes, do go on,' he frowned.

'She would not have approved of Gabriela,' she told him in a nervous rush, 'nor did she ever connect happiness with great wealth.'

'You are saying that she would have preferred Wendy's penniless father?'

Her father's face flashed before her eyes, bringing tenderness to her reply. 'I once heard her remark that he had a richness of heart that made wealth superfluous.'

He jerked erect, suddenly angry. 'Small wonder you were deceived! Your mother sounds to me to have been a very foolish woman and from what you have told me I must lay the blame for your misfortune firmly at her door! A mother should know enough of men to know immediately with whom she can entrust her daughter, but she seems to have been blindly sentimental, easily duped, and totally lacking in judgment!'

Without giving her time to protest, he ushered her out of the dining-room, left her while he collected her wrap, then guided her through the foyer and out of the hotel.

'Where are we going?' she gasped, running to keep up with his rangy stride.

A taxi slid to the curb and he bundled her into it, giving terse instructions to the driver. 'To the casino,' he snapped, then addressed her with sarcasm. 'Where superfluous wealth can buy superfluities . . .'

Though it was still comparatively early in the evening, the casino was thronged with people, elegant women bedecked with jewellery, and men who wore their affluence like a cloak, self-assured, negligent men to whom it seemed a matter of indifference whether they won or lost. Chandeliers glittered above the tables, their crystal droplets moving in the breeze rising in the wake of restless gamblers moving from one table to another in an effort to change their luck. Laconic croupiers drawled out winning numbers or flicked cards uppermost, betraying not the least sign of emotion whether the chips were raked inward or pushed outwards towards a lucky winner.

The atmosphere went to Serena's head, potent as a sparkling wine upon an untried palate. She gasped her thanks when Juan pushed a pile of chips into her hand.

'Try your luck,' he smiled, humour returning. 'On which table would you like to begin?'

'On the one with the spinning wheel, please,' she stammered, drawn as if magnetized by the lure of roulette. There was one seat vacant at the table and she slipped into it, feeling a flutter of nerves when Juan leant across her shoulder to instruct:

'Place some or all of your chips on whichever number you fancy.'

She began cautiously by placing three chips on number nine and was alert enough, when the croupier drawled: *'Rouge neuf!'* to realize that she had won. Expressionless faces around the table lightened a little when she twisted round to voice her excitement.

'I've won, Juan, I've won!'

'Then carry on, *amiga*,' he encouraged with an indulgent smile, 'there is no known antidote for beginner's luck.'

An hour later she was still playing, enjoying to the uttermost the thrill of seeing her modest pile of chips growing encouragingly larger as her chosen numbers were called. By this time Juan had gained a seat next to her and feeling almost embarrassed by her good fortune she whispered,

'Shall I stop now?'

'Not unless you wish to,' he counselled. 'When Fortune is favourable stride forward, for being a woman she favours the bold.'

So feeling both bold and slightly wicked, Serena pushed the whole of her chips on to the first number she had chosen and a murmur ran around the table as the wheel began to spin and the small white ball chattered around its perimeter, rapidly at first, then slower and slower until finally it faltered and fell into one of the troughs.

'*Rouge neuf!*' the croupier intoned, pushing across to her an enormous pile of chips.

She had no idea what monetary value they represented, but her eyes were enormous as shakily she told Juan, 'I don't think I want to play any more just now. Am I very rich?'

Ever so slightly, his mouth twitched. 'You are not quite an heiress yet, *chica*, but you have won a couple of thousand pounds of English money.'

'A couple of *thousand* . . . !' Colour rioted in her cheeks. 'But that's wonderful — I've never owned as much as a hundred!'

'So? Then perhaps you would be wise to hold on to what you have. As the fountain rises, so it must fall, and I would hate to see the delight vanish from your pretty face. How about a drink to celebrate? We must toast your good fortune in champagne.'

He cashed her chips before they left and it was not until he handed over to her an enormous wad of banknotes that realization truly struck. He glanced from the notes in his hands to her small evening purse.

'Shall I keep them for you?' he frowned. 'They might be safer in my charge.'

Serena stared transfixed at the bundle of notes, suddenly aware that for the first time in her life she possessed money, enough money to buy freedom, escape, a way out of the situation that was wearing down her nerves. In his hand Juan was holding more than enough to buy plane tickets for herself and Wendy, with sufficient left over to ensure that they would not starve while she searched for a home and a job in England.

Suddenly conscious of his narrow stare, she gasped, 'No, I'll keep them, thank you, there's plenty of room in my purse.'

'Very well,' he shrugged, handing over the lifeline which she clutched in shaking hands.

Outside the casino he hailed a taxi and she was still shaking when he handed her out of it to escort her into the nightclub in which he had chosen to round off their evening. The dim, discreetly intimate interior was decorated after the fashion of a tropical bar, a decor of waving palms, fishermen's nets strung out along the walls, exotic sea shells and bamboo tables and chairs set around a raised dais on which a trio of musicians were coaxing throbbing music from out of bass, drums and guitar.

Serena sat down in the chair Juan drew forward and eyed couples gyrating on the miniature dance floor while he ordered champagne. In a matter of minutes a bottle nestling in a bucket of crushed ice was delivered to their table, the cork popped, then the pale liquid sparkled into their glasses.

'Pale golden, outwardly cool yet seething with inner turbulence – the description could apply equally well to you, *chiquita*!' He raised his glass in mocking salute. 'What thoughts are disturbing your usually serene brow, are you plotting my downfall?'

Her hand holding the glass jerked with surprise, spilling some of the liquid on to the table. 'Of course not!' She marshalled her composure. Juan could read her mind with uncanny precision, seeming always to be one jump ahead of her. But this time he must not be allowed to guess the direction of her thoughts, it was imperative that his intuitive mind be lured in another direction. *Lured!* As she braved his needle-sharp eyes she reached a decision. Perhaps a change of tactics might disarm the too-perceptive man who, given the slightest cause to suspect, would stop at nothing to foil her plan.

Without the least qualm of conscience, she projected a shyly flirtatious look across the rim of her glass and whispered,

'Will you dance with me?'

She noted with satisfaction the quick upward shoot of his eyebrows, then felt trepidation when, with a glint of masculine conceit, he responded, 'But of course, *carestia*, I should be delighted!'

Only when she slipped into his arms did she realize how incredibly long it had been since last she had danced to romantic music in the arms of a young, presentable male.

But Juan proved himself to be more than just presentable. He was attentive, holding her close so that his lips brushed occasionally across her brow. He was romantic, in the way he halted to a sway, humming the haunting melody in her ear when the dance floor became crowded, examining with interest the confused blush suffusing her cheeks.

'Relax,' he murmured. 'You promised to forget that I am your husband and to treat me as a friend, remember? Does friendship warrant such stiff opposition?'

Reminded of the need to humour him, Serena forced fluidity into her limbs, finding it becoming gradually easier to enjoy following his lead as he led her expertly through the maze of dancers. She was laughing with sheer enjoyment when finally he guided her back to their table.

'Have some more champagne,' he urged, tilting

the slender-necked bottle until her glass was brimming.

She needed no extra stimulant, already she was bubbling over with effervescent excitement comparable with the sparkling, rapidly popping bubbles exploding in her glass. Yet she drank thirstily and with a quirk of satisfaction Juan again replenished her glass.

'Oh, better not!' she protested. 'I can feel the wine going to my head.'

'And I can feel you going to mine, *chiquita*,' he admitted, deliberately pinning her gaze. 'Rapidly, I find myself forgiving you your past and wishing that tonight was our first time of meeting. In a way it is,' he mused, reaching out to capture her hand in his. 'For the first time I am seeing you as a young and beautiful woman instead of a wife whose claim upon my freedom I bitterly resent. Your unfortunate experience has left little impression upon your innocent features – indeed, I am now beginning to understand the protective tenderness my grandfather always extends towards your sex, an attitude which previously I never felt was warranted. But perhaps your guilelessness is an inheritance from Eve who, even though she had no predecessor from whom to inherit wisdom, nevertheless found a way of bringing about the downfall of her supposedly superior mate.'

He was as good as admitting that he was intrigued, yet she was quick to sense the thread of suspicion running through his words. 'I have no wish to emulate Eve!' she protested, yet even as she spoke the denial she felt a flush of shame, remembering that her sole aim was to disarm him so completely he would forget the money burning a hole in her purse, thereby overlooking the use to which it might be put.

Frantic lashes swept down to hide her guilt when softly he murmured, 'I believe you, *carina*, your greatest guile is in having none at all.'

For the rest of the evening they shared a rapport which Serena felt as both a pain and an ecstasy. They danced to dreamy music, they talked, then they danced again, and each time she went into Juan's arms a little more willingly, each time he held her with a growing possessiveness. By the time they decided to leave she had become fearful that the situation she had engineered was becoming rapidly out of hand. She could sense within him a rising desire, and the rigid control he was exercising in order to keep their relationship as platonic as he had promised.

Each time their glances fused she saw lambent flame flare deep in his eyes, and his touch, though restrained, betrayed a compulsive urge to linger upon the curve of her waist and on the velvet softness of her arms. But the most shocking discovery of all was her own instinct to purr like a kitten at his stroke, to drown in the depths of his fathomless eyes, and to revel in the masculine virility she had bitter reason to distrust.

The streets were deserted as a taxi drove them back to the hotel, both settled comfortably in the back seat with Juan's arm circling her waist and her hair spread like a silken fan across the width of his shoulder. Not a word was spoken during the short drive, but within the confines of the taxi could be felt a build-up of raw tension, a dam of suppressed emotion that was crying out to be released lest some-one should suffer the consequences.

Once inside their suite Serena panicked and tried to escape by murmuring, 'It's late, if you'll excuse me I'll go straight to bed.'

She had almost passed him when a manacle of steel fastened around her wrist. 'Not yet, *cara*,' he drawled with a languor that was alarming. 'First we must share a nightcap.'

Needles of fire tingled along her arm as, in a small voice, she pleaded, 'I don't want any more to drink, Juan. Please let me go . . .'

His reply was physical. A swift jerk of his arm spun her into arms that pinioned her hard against his chest. 'You can't leave me now!' His low plea both thrilled and terrified. 'Stay with me tonight, *querida*! Let this evening be our *luna de miel*, not because my grandfather wished it but because we wish it ourselves!'

Their *honeymoon*! Her cry of dissent was crushed by lips seeking hungry response, not the gently en-couraging caress a man might place upon the lips of *novicia* but a plundering assault a woman such as Gabriela might have revelled in, but which Serena found degrading.

Like a snared animal she tried to struggle out of her trap, but her efforts seemed merely to amuse him.

'Come, *cara*,' he chastised in a throaty whisper, 'you know what is expected of you, give yourself to me and let me exorcize the ghost that haunts your heart. You are mortal, you *feel*,' he growled satisfaction when a shudder racked her slender frame, 'yet you are merely half alive. The other half lies buried with the dove who fluttered fleetingly into your life, his frail wings barely able to lift you to the edge of ecstasy. Do not be afraid of strength, *mi bella esposa*, the condor flies swift and strong to the very gates of heaven!'

'And releases when he is satisfied, plunging his prey into the pit of hell!' she gasped when his prowling lips swooped upon a nerve quivering in her throat. She pushed him hard, discovering in her fear a superhuman strength, and staggered away until the width of a table lay between them. 'So much for your promise, *señor*!' she derided, shaken to the very soul. 'Do all your *friends* hate you as much as I do?'

He jerked to a standstill, his expression incredulous, his eyes scouring her features as if doubting the sincerity of her words.

'I'm not sure I understand,' he enunciated slowly,

his amoral instincts curbed. 'Your attitude this even ing has been one of encouragement, even of fli tation, so why this sudden adoption of outrage virtue? I would imagine the events in your curiousl liberated past would have warned you of the folly c starting something you have no intention of fin ishing.' His drawl was as insulting as his words openly derisory of what he considered was a show o false prudery.

Serena suffered a painful blush, feeling immedi ately bracketed with a host of casual amours, and a a punishment decided to give a further turn to the screw.

'I grant you I made one mistake in the past señor, and have paid the price. But the experienc did, at least, teach me one thing – never to love again without first counting the cost.'

He pinned her with a long, hard look, then swept her a derisory bow. 'Love is said to be friendship with wings,' he jibed narrowly. 'It was foolish of me to forget your tendency to keep your pretty feet fixed firmly on the ground!'

CHAPTER TWELVE

THEY breakfasted together the next morning. When Serena joined Juan in the sitting-room she braced herself for a continuation of the sarcasm he had extended the previous evening, but to her relief he made no mention of the stormy interlude, although his manner was distant, his remarks terse and cutting.

As soon as he had finished eating he excused himself, setting her free for the day by remarking coldly, 'I am going out and will not be returning until this evening – no doubt you can keep yourself amused?'

She nodded and he strode away, leaving her to cope as best she could with an onrush of guilt. Although he had not accused, he could quite fairly have excused his behaviour of the previous evening on the grounds that he had received plenty of encouragement. Looking back, she felt fiercely ashamed. Yet the purpose behind her action remained as true as ever, and his absence for the day was a stroke of luck she had not envisaged.

Quickly she dressed, then after making inquiries at the reception desk hurried in the direction of the travel agency they had recommended. In one respect, at least, her plan had succeeded. Juan seemed to have completely forgotten about the money that was burning a hole in her pocket — either forgotten, or the fact had not yet registered that money represented escape from his dominance.

The greatest problem remaining was how to remove Wendy from the hacienda, but Serena decided she must take one step at a time, her most immediate aim being to find out if the money really was sufficient to cover both their air fares to England.

She was starry-eyed when she made her exit from the travel agency. In response to her request that the appropriate amount be deducted from the pile of currency, she had been agreeably surprised to find herself left with a substantial residue amounting, the clerk had assured her, to almost fifteen hundred pounds in English money.

She walked along the broad avenue, her mind teeming, and found a secluded corner facing the sea in which to concentrate the whole of her attention upon the finalizing of her plans. But however hard she thought, the vexing question of how to have Wendy transported from the hacienda seemed fated never to be resolved. She toyed with the idea of radioing Don Alberto on some pretext or other, asking him to send Wendy to join them at Viña del Mar, from where their escape would be comparatively simple. The Valdivias possessed two private planes, one, Juan's, in which they had travelled, and the other Don Alberto's, usually piloted by Pedro.

'How on earth,' she murmured in desperation, 'can I talk Don Alberto into doing as I ask without arousing his or Juan's suspicions?'

By lunchtime she was tired of wrestling with the problem and began wending her way back to the hotel. As she passed the reception desk on her way towards the lift a clerk hailed her.

'*Un momento, señora!* A cablegram has arrived for you and the *señor* – does it please you to take it now?'

Without interest she held out her hand for the envelope and as the lift whizzed her upwards she turned it over, staring vacantly at first, then intently as a notion struck her: The cable could only have been sent from someone at the hacienda, because only they knew where she and Juan were staying. The clerk had stated that the cablegram was addressed to them both, so obviously it could not be connected with matters of business.

Panic mounted as she tore open the envelope. The words it contained were an answer to her prayer.

Wendy fretting dreadfully. Will not be consoled. Am sending her to join you. Plane due Valparaiso airport 1400 hours approx.

1400 hours! Two o'clock! She snatched a glance at her watch and saw that it was almost twelve. Fiercely she pressed a button on the wall of the lift to halt its ascent, then pressed another to send it plummeting downward to the ground floor. When it finally stopped Serena ran straight out of the hotel and began frantically waving to attract the attention of passing taxi drivers. But each taxi seemed to be occupied and during the ensuing minutes she had time to rationalize her thoughts. Valparaiso was a mere fifteen minutes' drive away, and as Wendy's plane was not due to arrive for two hours she would have ample time in which to pack a few belongings so that when Wendy was finally handed over she would have no need to return to the hotel but could take a taxi straight to the huge, bustling Santiago airport within which they could lose themselves for as long as necessary before boarding a plane for England!

Curious eyes followed her re-entry into the hotel, but she was so full of single-minded purpose they made no impression. It took less than twenty minutes of precious time to cram all she needed into a suitcase which, in a more composed manner, she then carried into the lift, past the watching clerk in reception, and out of the hotel. This time she was fortunate enough to engage the first passing taxi and with a sigh of relief she sank into the back, feeling utterly drained as she instructed the driver: 'Valparaiso airport – and please hurry!'

When they arrived she paid off the taxi and found a seat in the airport lounge which gave her a good view of the runway. For what seemed an aeon she fretted, glancing every minute or so at her watch as it crept ever so slowly towards the stated time of the plane's arrival. Juan could not possibly know of her whereabouts; even if he arrived back at the hotel sooner than he intended and was told of the cablegram he would have no knowledge of what it contained. Yet the threat of his presence loomed so strongly that she could not keep her eyes from straying towards the airport entrance. Magazines lay unopened on her lap as, moving her head constantly from side to side, she glanced from the airstrip to the doorway through which she felt certain Juan would stride at any moment.

At last, to her enormous relief, she saw the Valdivia plane swooping down to land and she jumped up and ran outside to wait in a fever of impatience until the wheels touched the runway and it taxied to a standstill. She broke into a run and when Bella stepped from the plane holding Wendy in her arms Serena was there to receive her, panting with exertion, almost incoherent in her efforts to thank Bella for escorting the child.

'Oh, it was nothing, *señora*!' Bella assured her, her brow wrinkling with concern. 'The poor little *niña* has been desolate during your absence. We tried everything we could think of to console her, to amuse her, to keep her mind from her beloved *mamaita*, but to no avail. Even El Conde himself could not stem the flow of tears, and it was he who finally decided she should be brought to you.'

'Poor darling!' Serena held out her arms and Wendy's lacklustre eyes immediately brightened. Her small pinched face was proof enough of Bella's words, but at first sight of Serena a smile broke like a ray of sunshine through clouds and she almost bounced into her waiting arms. 'Oh, sweetheart, how good it is to hold you,' Serena murmured, burying her face in a riot of baby curls. 'I'll never leave you again, I promise, we'll be together now for always!'

She returned a wave from the smiling Pedro, still seated in the cockpit, and as he was making no move to leave it, she questioned uncertainly,

'What are your plans, Bella – have you been instructed to stay?'

'Only if you require my services, *señora*, otherwise I am to return to the hacienda.'

'Then go. I have no need of you here,' Serena urged.

Bella's puzzled glance roamed the airstrip, obviously wondering at the absence of Don Juan, but obediently she clambered back into the plane without asking the question trembling on her lips and shortly afterwards the engine revved and the plane began moving along the runway with ever-gathering speed. Serena forced herself to wait until it had taken off, then she hurried inside the airport building, clamouring fear and relief making her feel weak at the knees.

Carrying Wendy, who was nuzzling delightedly into her neck, on one arm and clutching her suitcase with the other, she all but ran outside to the taxi rank and stammered urgently to a waiting driver,

'Santiago airport, please!'

Inwardly fuming, she waited while courteously he stowed away her suitcase and settled her and Wendy into the back seat of the taxi. It seemed, she fretted, she had chosen the most slow-moving and negligent driver in the whole of Valparaiso, but at long last the taxi drew away from the airport, and only then did her tense body relax and the tight, anxious frown disappear from her face.

'We're on our way, darling!' She disengaged Wendy's clutching fist from her hair to give her a delighted hug. 'Soon we'll be out of reach of the dominating Valdivias!'

As swiftly as the wheels transporting them inland, her thoughts began to spin. Release, if she were lucky, was a few short hours away and even if she were unfortunate enough to have to wait until tomorrow for a flight home, no more than twenty-four hours away. Time enough when she arrived in England to worry about how to seek release from the bonds of marriage which legally, at least, kept her chained to Juan's side. It would be a mere formality, she felt sure, to have the unconsummated marriage annulled so that when eventually she did meet the man whose presence used to haunt her dreams there would be no obstacle in the path of their happiness.

She tried to picture him – the man whose features her imagination had never completely outlined, but his face remained a blur. Yet the virtues she had cherished were projected as strongly as ever; a strong character, one on whose strength she could lean with confidence, a maker of decisions, a man of inflexible will and matching confidence, a masterly, virile mate!

Juan's face flashed before her eyes and was swiftly rejected. Her ideal man must be possessed of tenderness, and this emotion she had found to be totally lacking in Juan. Last night she had attracted him, but only because she was the only woman available. He had been in the mood for a flirtatious affair and any presentable female would have sufficed, even the second-hand bride whose previous usage he had been prepared to overlook – but for one night only, after which his resentment would have increased a thousandfold. The arrogant, masterly Valdivias would share with no man – not his land, not his riches, and especially not his wife!

A couple of hours later she and Wendy were established in the departure lounge of Santiago airport. The tickets had been purchased, her suitcase handed over, and all they had to do was wait until their flight number was called – a matter of two hours, she had been informed, provided there was no unforeseen delay.

Wendy was becoming fractious and with a start of guilt Serena realized it was some time since the child had eaten. She herself was not the least bit hungry, the very thought of food nauseated her. 'How I envy you your sweet, uncomplicated outlook on life,' she ruffled Wendy's curls. 'Come along, my pet, we'll get you some food.'

Inside the airport restaurant she headed for the least conspicuous table and after settling Wendy in a high chair ordered scrambled eggs for both of them, and while they waited to be served pushed her chair as far behind a screen of potted palms as was possible. Her edginess was so acute she could barely handle her knife and fork when the meal arrived, so after a couple of attempts she discarded it entirely and concentrated upon spooning egg into Wendy's appreciative mouth. The baby would not be hurried, but began playing hide and seek with the spoon once the first pangs of hunger had been assuaged, buttoning her lips against the approaching spoon, then banging ferociously on the tray of her high chair when Serena withdrew the food.

The feeding operation took so long Serena was astonished to hear their flight number called.

'Goodness!' She jumped to her feet. 'It's time to go!' She ran from the restaurant hauling a protesting Wendy beneath her arm, and began weaving her way through the crowds, embarrassed by, but determined to ignore, Wendy's protesting screams. She reached the appropriate gate where a queue had already begun to form. Outside on the runway the waiting aircraft was revving up, a wonderful sight, the magic carpet that was to transport them back to the world of sanity Serena had so recklessly abandoned.

As a smiling stewardess began ushering her charges towards the aircraft Serena stepped forward, her eyes fixed firmly upon her objective, so intent upon her goal that a detaining grip on her elbow barely registered.

Through a roaring in her ears she heard Juan's smooth charm directed towards the stewardess. 'My wife has changed her mind, she will not now be travelling on this flight.' Anchored to the spot by leaden feet, Serena watched the crocodile of passengers disappear from sight, too utterly dismayed to project even one word of protest through frozen lips. He allowed her to watch until the plane had taken off before grimly making comment.

'My opinion of you has never been high, but until today I had not thought of you as a cheat!'

Serena turned upon him such a look of despair he winced. 'I almost made it . . .!' she choked. '*Why* couldn't you have let me go home?'

'It would have made no difference if you had gone,' he clenched. 'I would have torn England apart to find you!'

She was too upset to wonder at the whiteness around his compressed lips and the nerve pulsating madly in his jaw – a barometer registering the extent of his anger.

Afterwards, she had no recollection of the short flight back to Valparaiso, during which she remained huddled in a seat holding Wendy's slumbering warmth close to her frozen body while Juan

158

concentrated his full attention upon piloting the plane.

Upon their arrival at the hotel, at Juan's request, a cot was placed in Serena's bedroom and the still slumbering child was laid gently inside.

'Now!' He swung her round to face him. 'You have some explaining to do!' Unkind fingers gouged her shoulders as he marched her into the sitting-room and thrust her unceremoniously down on to the settee. Serena shrank from his towering bulk and felt a fear deeper than he had previously aroused when tightly he clenched,

'Never in my life before have I felt an urge to thrash one of your sex! How dare you do this to me – you, my wife, have deliberately flouted my will! Imagine the scorn of my friends had I been forced to return meekly to the hacienda and explain that my wife had left me!'

Her numbness was pierced by the heat of his anger, arousing an answering spark. 'I am *not* your wife!' She flung back her head, dislodging a golden screen of hair from flushed cheeks. 'And I neither know nor care what your friends might think, *señor*!'

He leant forward, pinioning her shoulders against the back of the settee. 'You try me too far, *mi bella esposa*,' he chilled with menace. 'It appears I have been too lenient in the past, too conscious of your need of time in which to erase from your heart the image of the man you think you loved. Now I see

159

that my consideration was not appreciated. Deep down, like others of your sex, you prefer to be robbed rather than to give willingly.'

When he released her she jumped to her feet, shaken by the implied threat. 'What do you mean to do? What further torment have you in mind?'

'Torment?' Juan drawled with eyes of flint. 'No torment, I assure you, simply a tasteful dinner served here in our suite followed by a restful evening together getting to know one another more — intimately! Meanwhile, I suggest you freshen up. Wear the cream-coloured dress in which you look like an innocent madonna — and the sapphires, to remind me that what I take I have paid for.'

Long after he had swung on his heel and left, Serena remained rooted to the spot, knowing she had reached the hour of reckoning and that there was nothing she could do to prevent Juan carrying out the sentence he had deemed fit punishment for her crime. Wearily she retired to her bedroom to do as he had instructed, and knew his mood had not softened when later he strode inside her room, his features chilled into lines of grimness, his dark head outstanding with pride above a white dinner jacket superbly tailored to his muscular shoulders.

'Dinner is waiting to be served,' he informed the pale, frightened ghost striving to appear composed.

'I'm ready,' she whispered, feeling like a condemned woman being led to her execution.

The meal, served by a hovering waiter, was as tasteless as bread and water, yet Serena went through the motions of eating, even managing to respond to his light conversation. Her frozen state sustained her right through the meal when finally, at Juan's command, the waiter withdrew, leaving her to pour out the coffee. She did so with a trembling hand, refusing with a shake of her head the balloon glass of brandy he placed at her elbow.

'Drink it!' he rapped. 'It will fetch the colour back to your cheeks.'

But not the hope to my heart! she thought wildly, too scared to disobey.

When she had downed the last drop he joined her on the settee, sitting so close he could feel her trembling like a captured bird. 'Are you cold?' His hand scorched her uncovered shoulder.

'No,' she gasped, feeling his breath fanning her cheek.

'Good,' he murmured thickly, drawing her closer, 'then my task will be made that much easier.'

She did not resist when his mouth stormed hers, nor did she respond — at least not until his anger-inspired kisses became less punishing and were surprisingly replaced by a gentle tenderness that soothed her ragged emotions and routed all thought of hatred from her heart.

Slowly she began to respond, moving her lips in a petal-soft caress across his cheek, murmuring small broken endearments through lips crushed into life by his kisses.

Juan lifted her into his arms, carried her into his room, then kicked shut the door before striding across to lower her gently onto the bed. Without hesitation her arms opened to receive him and with a groan he gathered her into a fierce embrace, then proceeded, as promised, to transport her to the very gates of heaven.

Hours later she left him sleeping soundly and tiptoed silently back to her own bed, where she lay staring at the ceiling until breaking dawn sent fingers of light creeping across its blank surface.

CHAPTER THIRTEEN

WENDY awoke early and it was a relief to Serena to have to minister to her needs, occupation for her hands if not her mind. When the toddler had been washed and dressed she took her into the hotel grounds where they wandered along paths bordered with flowers, pausing now and then to admire a particularly breathtaking splash of colour, or to drink in the heady scent of dew-laden blossoms. No one but themselves seemed to be astir and within the peaceful solitude her thoughts found freedom to run riot.

Juan had yet to be faced. She would die of shame if he should taunt her, and the thought of facing his inevitable satisfaction was torture worse than death. Before Wendy had wakened she had showered in a cool stinging spray, hoping to wash away the imprints of his possessive hands from her still burning body. But the impressions still remained and the memory of her own response, the broken endearments that had whispered past her lips and, worse still, the way in which she had abandoned herself to the pain of all-consuming passion, made her want to flee from the hotel and drown her humiliation beneath the cleansing coolness of the heaving Pacific.

But she had Wendy to consider. For her sake she had to face reality – and reality was Juan, who even now would be waiting in their suite for her appearance at breakfast. Sounds of activity began drifting from the region of the hotel kitchens as slowly she retraced her steps and re-entered the hotel. Outside the doorway of their suite she hesitated, then just as her hand was reaching out the door was flung open and Juan appeared, glowering on the threshold. White-faced, his shower-damp hair run through with agitated fingers, he grated,

'Where have you been?'

'Walking . . . in the grounds . . .' she stammered, unable, now that the moment was upon her, to meet his eyes. Daring to look no higher than the second button on his shirt, she wondered at his tense leanness, his aura of suppressed anger, and thought for a brief moment that his explosive attitude was caused by concern.

He quickly disabused her. 'I want you to pack immediately, we are leaving for the hacienda directly after breakfast.'

'Very well,' she said flatly, moving past him into the sitting-room. She would have gone straight to her bedroom, but Wendy had other ideas. With her favourite man in the vicinity she had no intention of letting pass an opportunity of continuing their flirtation.

'Coo . . . o!' she gurgled, holding out her arms, almost leaping from Serena's grasp in her eagerness to reach him.

A quiver that was almost a smile broke the stern symmetry of Juan's mouth. He reached out to take her. *'Buen' dias, bella niña!* It is gratifying to know that at least one female member of my family does not consider me beneath contempt. Would that you could convey a little of your attitude to your beloved *mamaita . . .'*

The lack of heat in his tone, the faint stress he had placed upon his last word affected Serena with sudden dismay. The moment passed, however, and she dismissed her suspicion as a figment of over-sensitive conscience. There was no possible way he could know!

They pretended to eat breakfast in an atmosphere of unbearable tension until finally Juan pushed away his plate in order to outline in detail the course he intended her to take.

'When we return to the hacienda you must endeavour to hide your obvious animosity. Yesterday, I spoke to my grandfather by radio,' he disclosed, supplying without question the means by which he had found out the contents of the cablegram, 'and he informed me that he is ready to begin the holiday he had planned immediately we return. Once he has left the hacienda you can be as cool and distant as you wish, but until then I must insist that you be as diplomatic as possible. I fully expect – indeed he himself hinted – that before he leaves for Spain he will sign over to me the entire control of the hacienda. His lawyers are at this very moment drawing up the necessary papers, and once my position has been legally established the bargain we struck can be considered terminated – technically, at least,' he hastened to add. 'You realize, of course, that the freedom you seek cannot be immediately granted. That will take time, but time is on our side, we are both young enough not to begrudge my grandfather the spurious satisfaction of thinking he has judged correctly, for the few years that are left to him.'

Serena had listened with bowed head, never once lifting her eyes from her plate. 'Are you asking me or telling me that I must co-operate?' she choked. Then with a spurt of bravery, 'But then you cannot *demand* this of me, for once I am in a position to make up my own mind without heeding your co-ercion. Indeed,' she realized with sudden insight, 'your whole future hangs upon whether or not I decide to do as you ask!'

Juan nodded glacial acknowledgment. 'It does. But I think you now realize how foolish you would be to oppose me.'

Yes, she was fully aware what a merciless adversary he could be. Already he had dominated her body as he could dominate her will – but not her heart, that cold, lifeless object was too deeply entombed in ice ever to be stirred.

'Very well, I will do as you ask,' she complied with a trace of bitterness. 'I have little choice, considering how much more expert you are than I at achieving your ends.'

Her decision pleased him. At least his voice sounded a little less severe, even slightly indulgent.

'You *are* rather amateurish in that respect,' he agreed. 'Practically everyone in the hotel knew by your attitude that you had received news of some significance. I was informed immediately I returned of your precipitate flight, complete with baggage, and it needed little detective work on my part to discover your destination. In a way, I blame myself. I delivered the weapon straight into your hands, did I not? I ought to have foreseen the use to which the money would be put, and also,' he suddenly grated, 'I should have guessed that your flirtatious advances were nothing more than a deliberate ploy to keep me off the scent.'

Serena looked up, then quickly away, confused by bleak, expressionless features that ought to have been registering satisfaction but which instead were a controlled mask indicating the presence of some savage inner emotion.

She rose from the table murmuring an excuse, but as she walked towards her room Juan addressed a ragged question to her retreating back. 'Before we leave ... is there something I should know which neither you nor my grandfather has seen fit to tell me?'

She spun round, betraying visible astonishment and a quick glint of fear. 'No ... why do you ask?'

His steady gaze stripped her of the ability to pretend, making her defenceless against the flood of guilt that stained her cheeks.

He walked up to her and lightly touched her cheek. 'Flags of shame or of innocence, I wonder ᴜ ꜱ ʜ?' he murmured, then spun on his heel.

The flight back to the hacienda was swift and silent and when the plane touched down on the airstrip Don Alberto was waiting to greet them.

'Ah, Serena! I was so sorry to have to send *la niña* to you. I hope my action was not responsible for cutting short your holiday?'

She returned his kiss. 'We were ready to return, life at the hacienda is so pleasant it makes a holiday unnecessary.'

A beam of pleasure spread across his face. 'How happy I am to hear you say so, *cara*, but you enjoyed the break, did you not?' His glance sped from her to Juan. 'You made the most of your short honeymoon?'

'Indeed, yes,' Juan replied dryly, and his grandfather laughed, noting the confused sweep of lashes across Serena's cheeks.

'*Bueno!* Then now we can get down to business!' He turned to Serena. 'I know you will understand when I ask you to excuse us both for a while, my dear. My lawyer is waiting at the house with some papers that require both our signatures. That in itself should not take long, but there are many matters which my grandson and I must discuss before I leave tomorrow on the holiday I have been promising myself for years but which, for reasons no longer relevant, I have had to defer. But no longer! Tomorrow, after the rodeo, I will definitely be on my way.'

Bella and Carmen, Serena later discovered, could talk of nothing but the rodeo which was to take place the following day – an annual event, they told her, during which the *huasos* displayed their incredible abilities as horsemen. 'Training and skill count as much as daring and strength,' Bella assured her with shining eyes. 'Rodeos are very gay, people drink a lot, eat a lot, and sing a lot and the music of guitars, harps and accordions fills the air. The action begins for me,' she breathed, 'when *el toro* gallops into the arena !'

But Serena paid little heed to their babbling. Her mind was set upon more important matters – the signing over of the hacienda into Juan's hands, Don Alberto's departure and the lines on which her life would run once his buffeting presence was removed from the house. She had no doubt how Juan would fill his evenings once he became free of his grandfather's gimlet eye. Gabriela's presence seemed to hover in the very air around them, as if projected by telepathic thought across the few miles separating her from the man she loved.

'*She can have him with my blessing!*' Serena was surprised at the vehemence of her own outburst, surprised to find her teeth clenched and her fingernails digging deep into her palms. Sharply, she chided aloud, much to Wendy's dismay, 'Oh, for heaven's sake, put the man out of your mind!' Then as Wendy's bottom lip began to quiver she swooped to comfort her. 'Don't cry, darling, I was scolding myself, not you! But on second thoughts,' she eyed her severely, 'you could take my advice – your adoration of that man is far too blatant, what you see in him I'll never know!'

Wendy hiccupped, then chuckled, and Serena just had to join in – then found that for some unknown reason she could not stop. Her laughter pealed out like a carillon of bells, reaching the ears of the three men engrossed in business in the study below.

Don Alberto lifted his head and listened, then with a flourish he inscribed his signature on the last of the documents. 'Your wife is happy, my son,' he smiled at Juan. 'Her laughter endorses my belief that I have come to the right decision. Come now,' he beamed, 'admit that I did well in bringing her here. Tell me you no longer resent my well-meaning meddling in your affairs. Whatever you might be tempted to profess to the contrary, the alliance has worked well, your wife is obviously ecstatically happy.'

Juan nodded agreement, but his answering smile did not quite reach his eyes. He had no intention of sharing his suspicion that the girl whose laughter his grandfather found so pleasing probably had hysterical tears streaming down her cheeks.

'I must bow to your superior judgment, Grandfather. Once again you have proved yourself an expert matchmaker. In time I hope to justify your trust in myself as a worthy successor.'

'Then let us celebrate my last evening with a memorable dinner, so that while I am away I shall have a happy memory to console me during my absence.'

Juan nodded agreement. 'In that case, I had better warn Serena to wear her prettiest dress.'

She followed his instructions to the letter and appeared before dinner, composed and beautiful, seeming to float in a cloud of blue chiffon, her slim shoulders squared bravely as she prepared to act out the final chapter of the deceiving charade.

'My grandfather must be left in no doubt of our attachment,' Juan had informed her earlier, 'so if you find my affectionate advances distasteful the fact that they are the last I will ever impose upon you should make them easier to bear.'

She consoled herself with these words when, as she entered the salon where Juan and his grandfather were drinking *aperitifs*, Juan put down his glass and advanced to greet her with a kiss. She could barely repress a shudder when his hand descended upon her waist.

'You are looking divinely beautiful, *mi esposa*,' he murmured loudly enough to reach his grandfather's ears, before bending to imprint a slow, deliberate kiss upon her upturned mouth.

If this is a foretaste of what's to come I shall never last out the evening! Serena panicked.

Projecting a smile of pride, Juan presented her to his grandfather, who rose to bestow a second kiss that was like cool balm upon a scald. 'Tonight I am very happy, *niña*.' His bright eyes traced her sweetly solemn face. 'Not to every man is given the satisfaction of participating in a *buen' amor* – twice.'

A *love match*! Serene managed to smile as she returned his kiss. 'Not every man is as wise and understanding as yourself, Abuelito,' she complimented, feeling self-contempt knotting her stomach.

'You are content with this grandson of mine?' he urged. 'Ah, but then,' he embraced her, visibly casting aside all doubt, 'I have no need to ask, when I can see for myself how very much in love you both are.'

As if sensing her inner rebellion, Juan quickly stepped forward and swung an arm around her waist. 'Let me pour you a drink, *querida*. What would you like – some of your favourite champagne?'

Serena hated his deliberate reference to an evening she wanted to forget. This was his way of reminding her that she was no stranger to deceit and that scruples were abortive in this last stage of the game. She felt a sudden reckless urge to outwit him, to disconcert his smooth urbanity, and from somewhere she dredged a spirited response.

'Yes, please, darling. Do you remember the last time we drank champagne? It was the night I had that wonderful win at the casino. Afterwards we danced the night away, and when we returned to our hotel you were in such a romantic mood.'

Her heart dipped when he returned her bland teasing with a gimlet stare, but his recovery was immediate. Quickly he fenced, 'That night will never be erased from my memory, for how could I ever forget your sweetness? You managed to combine the wiliness of Eve with the flirtatiousness of a coquette – but then for me that has always been your greatest appeal, this ability you possess to drive a man to distraction wondering which pose you will decide to adopt next.'

As they exchanged smiles of mutual dislike Don Alberto's delighted laughter rang in their ears. 'There, did I not assure you, *niña*, that my grandson could not resist a mystery? Even when he was a boy, nothing could deter him from completing a complicated jigsaw and even his favourite outdoor pursuits took second place to an unsolved puzzle. Come, let us eat, happiness has sharpened my appetite, I intend enjoying to the full this last family meal!'

Somehow, as the leisurely dinner progressed, Serena managed to hang on to her spirited defence, continuing to answer Juan's pointed remarks with a

173

sweet reasonableness run through with innuendo only he could interpret. Don Alberto remained sublimely unaware, entertained by the swift interchange of words which, had he but known it, were being thrown like weapons between opponents. Affectionate masks hid their rancour as the barbs flew between them, sometimes finding their mark to inflict intense pain that had to be hidden beneath a still brighter smile or, in Juan's case, by deliberate displays of affection which, as she prodded him into anger, grew more and more outrageous.

The culmination came, as it was fated to, in a clash of temperament all the more intense because it had to be kept secret from the elderly gentleman dozing in an armchair, replete with helpings of his favourite food, garnished with a sauce of ill-founded contentment.

They were standing close together at the window, looking out across the moonlit garden, presenting to the old gentleman who occasionally lifted one sleepy eyelid a picture of devotion – lovers engrossed in togetherness. But as Juan's intimidating shadow loomed over her Serena felt a tightening of tension and a conviction that if she were not to shatter Don Alberto's illusions the dreadful evening must be brought to a swift end. As his head lowered solicitously she repulsed him in a fierce whisper. 'I've had enough, I'm going to my room!'

'That is the first sensible decision you've made all evening,' he returned in a sibilant hiss.

His vehemence startled her and she would have jerked away had not his detaining arm snaked around her waist. She shrank from the glittering eyes boring into her face. The devil in him was aroused, his temper stretched to snapping point. Between clenched teeth he projected a command that threatened reprisal if she dared to disobey.

'You have played your part to perfection, but then when you decide to cheat you cheat well. Now *go*, for God's sake *go*!'

Serena stumbled past the sleeping Don Alberto and up to her room, where for hours she lay in the great solitary bed staring, her mind numb. Then around midnight, long after the rest of the household had retired, she heard footsteps on the floor of the stone *plazuela* beneath her window, footsteps accompanied by the jingle of spurs progressing in the direction of the stables. Propped up on one elbow, she strained her ears and a few minutes later heard the soft fall of hooves as a horse was led from its box. Then came the jingle of harness and spurs as the rider mounted and a muffled trotting of hooves as gradually the horse gathered speed and began galloping away.

She sank back into her pillows feeling indefinable pain, a suffering far worse than that he had taken such pleasure in inflicting earlier, a puzzling sense of nausea that was somehow connected with the conviction that the call of Gabriela had been heard and was even now in the process of being answered.

CHAPTER FOURTEEN

THE *huasos* began gathering soon after dawn and sounds of much activity coming from the direction of the corral awakened Serena. An arena, padded with cane all around the sides, was being erected. It looked like a giant laundry basket, she thought later, when curiosity drove her down to investigate. The *huasos* in their colourful ponchos, broad-brimmed sombreros and tight-fitting black leathers had a proud, dignified appearance as they sat tall in the saddle. Man and horse were part of a team, one indispensable to the other, so consequently the animals were trained to a nicety, well treated and very well cared for.

They were busy, but still had time to spare for a wave of greeting towards *la bella Inglesa* and the child who more and more each day was beginning to resemble her fair-haired, blue-eyed *mamaita*. Soon, other riders began arriving from adjacent haciendas, competitors in the many rodeo events. Then cars began rolling up to disgorge the élite of the district, Don Alberto's compatriots and their families, sharp-eyed mothers and dutiful daughters to whom the day was yet another social occasion in which to seek out and select prospective husband material.

Of Juan Serena had seen no sign, so that when the first event was announced and Don Alberto appeared at her side, questioning his absence, she could only stammer an evasive reply.

'He's about somewhere . . . perhaps down at the corral organizing the events?'

'Organizing?' he snorted. 'Preparing to participate, more like! Each year I grow more fearful of the dangers, but he laughs and goes his own way. Not that I would have him any different,' he relented, 'he is as he was born to be — headstrong, wilful, and proud.'

In spite of her intention to appear indifferent, Serena began searching the now considerable crowd circling the arena for a sight of Juan's dark head. Then, impatient of her own weakness, she stared ahead, concentrating upon the first of the events, a competition in which the *huasos* vied to chase, lasso and hogtie a steer in the fastest number of seconds.

The second event was bareback riding, and she and Wendy were escorted by Don Alberto to a narrow, railed-off alley leading off the arena where, behind a barred gate, a blindfold horse was being held steady to enable a rider to mount. The alley was not wide enough to allow the wildly kicking stallion to turn around, consequently it had no other outlet for its temper other than to lash out wickedly with its rear hooves while the rider jumped swiftly on to its back.

The second he was seated the blindfold was whipped from the stallion's eyes and the gate flung open, granting a way of escape to the mean-looking, powerfully-rearing horse carrying its whip-slim rider. Serena caught a mere glimpse of the reckless-eyed man as the stallion charged past her into the arena to be greeted by cheers from a wildly encouraging crowd. Her mouth went dry as with enormous eyes she watched Juan's body bent like a spring, first backward, then forward, as determined to stay put as the horse was determined to unseat him.

Her choked protest went unheard in the roar that erupted when the horse jumped high into the air to land foursquare on the ground with fearful impetus. Pain jarred her body as if she, and not Juan, were the rider. She closed her eyes, fearful of seeing his virile body being trampled beneath frantic hooves, but at the sound of a second cheer she opened them to discover him, still seated in the saddle, being escorted out of the arena by two riders, his dark head tossed back, his white teeth flashing a triumphant grin to the applauding spectators.

Shaken to the depths, she moved as far out of sight of the arena as her shaking legs would carry her. On the perimeter of the crowd she found an unoccupied bench and she sank down, allowing Wendy to slide out of her arms to play in the grass around her feet. She tried to marshall her chaotic thoughts, to come to terms with the truth that had struck with the impact of flaying hooves, jolting her into facing a fact danger had forced to the surface, a fact which, once having been acknowledged, was refusing to remain hidden.

She was in love with the man she had thought she hated!

Suddenly her ideal man had features: a merciless, passionate mouth that could melt into tenderness; brooding eyes, one minute fathomless, the next full of storming temperament; a fine blade of nose with arrogantly distended nostrils; lean tanned cheeks that creased deeply whenever he smiled that devastating smile capable of making her heart turn a somersault! His voice echoed in her ears, reminding her in a low, sensuous tone of the sweet endearments he had smothered against her cheeks, her hair, the curve of throat and shoulders, on the night that had begun as punishment and ended in confusing rapture.

With a moan she covered her eyes, trying to blot out the memory, wondering how she could have been so blind as to mistake weltering emotions, trembling limbs and storm-racked senses for symptoms of hatred. How long had she loved him? She traced back to their very first meeting and knew, with a sense of shock, that even then attraction had reared its turbulent head, thriving since under the guise of hatred until sudden danger had found it another name. *Love!* She loved him so much that the very thought of hooves pounding his body into the dust was enough to impel a spurt of scalding tears. Remorselessly she examined her newly-discovered love until there was no room left in her heart for pride. She dwelt upon the ecstatic hours they had shared, feeling neither shame nor remorse, merely possessive longing and a terrible fear that she might never again know the glory of loving and being loved by him.

As blindly she relived the memory of that night she failed, in her absorption, to notice Wendy's red-trewed figure wriggling towards the fence behind which she could hear the voice of her favourite man. Awareness came too late. She started back to life just in time to see Wendy's heels disappearing through a gap in the fence just big enough to allow her entry. She tried to call out, but horror had frozen her voice to a croak, so she began to run and when she reached the fence heard a gasp of dismay rising simultaneously from the throats of the watching crowd. Her heartbeats stopped, suspended by the sight that met her eyes.

In the centre of the arena Juan, astride a mount, was concentrating his will upon a savagely resentful, ferocious-looking bull. Transfixed, Serena watched him ride towards the beast, stop him at a point along a wall marked by flags, then turn him round. Then he began driving him in the opposite direction, again without using force, demonstrating the ability he had learned on the range to sort out vast herds of cattle for branding, fattening or shipping, of making cattle do whatever he wanted merely by crowding them into line.

But this time the spectators' startled eyes were not focused upon his skill. Horror-stricken, they were watching a tiny red-trewed figure crawling across the arena oblivious of danger, anxious to attract the attention of the man whose back was turned upon her, vexingly preoccupied with his task.

Then Serena screamed, a high-pitched scream of terror that pierced Juan's absorption, spinning him round in the saddle.

'Por mi vida!' His exclamation cracked across the stunned arena as, sharp as his words, he swung from the saddle and began running towards the gurgling child.

It was the opportunity the enraged bull had been waiting for. Immediately his adversary's back was turned he began a snorting, wild-eyed charge, his lowered head with sharp-pointed horns promising death to his tormentor.

Serena saw Juan's frantic race to pluck Wendy from the ground, then as the charging bull advanced to within mere feet of its prey she closed her eyes and slid into a dead faint that blotted out the inevitable agonizing climax.

She was unaware of *huasos* who, galvanized into action, threw a protective ring around Juan and the child before forcing the bull back to its pen. Nor was she aware of being picked up and carried into the house, of servants scurrying to answer demented calls for brandy and wet towels with which to bathe her forehead. All she knew as she struggled out of the pit of agony was that she had lost everything in life dear to her, and the first name that moaned past her colourless lips was: '*Juan!*'

'I'm here, *querida*!' The strangled reply must, she thought, be an echo from heaven. Heavy lashes lifted from tormented eyes and in that first split second she was too confused to hide her feelings – the great swell of joy, eyes with veil torn apart that blazed brilliant relief at the sight of him.

'Rest now, *cara*,' he encouraged softly. 'You have experienced a great shock – I promise we will both return later when you are feeling stronger.'

With both Bella and Carmen bustling around her bed she did not feel able to reply freely, but her heart was in her eyes as she watched him carry Wendy to the doorway, then turn for a second to cast an inscrutable look towards her before retreating slowly out of the cool shutter-dimmed room, leaving a consoling jingle of spurs in his wake.

She clung to the sound long after he had gone, and it remained with her in the depths of shock-ridden sleep as a constant reminder that there would be nothing to fear when finally she awoke. But hours later when she felt able to slip from the bed and into a dressing-gown she found that she did feel fear – fear of the vulnerable towards the strong, fear that Juan might mock her no longer secret feelings, fear of the ruthlessness with which he might wield the whip of power over her defenceless emotions.

It was early evening when he returned. The arena had long since been dismantled, the people dispersed, and as she sat in a chair by an open window a blossom-laden breeze lifted tendrils of fine hair from her forehead and stroked cooling balm across her hot cheeks. She knew the moment he entered, yet did not stir. He had recently showered and a tangy hint of cologne mingling with the aroma of a recently-smoked cheroot drifted a warning beneath her nostrils.

He spoke quietly so as not to startle her, but though she made no pretence at surprise she did not turn her head but continued staring blindly out of the window.

'Carmen tells me you are almost fully recovered, but if you do not feel like talking I will come back later.'

Serena breathed in deeply; what had to be said must be said and now was as good a time as any.

'You may stay if you wish. Please be seated.'

If he was disconcerted by the formality of her tone he made no sign, but disturbed her by choosing to sit on the broad windowledge directly in front of her. Still she refused to meet his eyes and fastened her gaze upon the brown column of throat left exposed by a casual, open-necked shirt. Her fingernails dug into her palms as delicately he began to probe.

'The shock you received must have been great

when it caused you to faint. Did you think the child had been harmed?'

With a sickening jolt she became aware for the first time that Wendy, darling, sweet baby, had, at the actual moment of danger, been secondary in her mind. Her own heartlessness caused her a shudder which he was quick to notice.

'Are you cold in that flimsy thing? Shall I fetch you a warmer wrap?'

'No, thank you.' She trembled, clutching the fine cotton gown closer. 'I'll be all right in a second, the events of this afternoon were so ... so traumatic ...'

'They were,' Juan agreed, sending her a keen, searching glance.

Suddenly she could bear it no longer – the impending inquisition, the amusement he must be striving hard to conceal. 'You know, don't you? You know, so why pretend?'

Swiftly he moved, bending over her, close, very close. 'I know what, *querida*? Tell me what it is that I know?'

'You know,' her voice broke on a sob, 'you know, you beast, that I'm in love with you!'

There, it was out in the open, it had actually been said! The admission hung heavy in the air between them.

Calmly he drew her to her feet yet, incredibly, she felt a tremor run through him as very gently he pressed her head against his shoulder.

'And is that all I need to know, Serena?'

His nearness was distracting, she could feel the heavy beat of his heart through the thin material of her gown and sensed a force within him straining at the leash yet kept in determined check while he waited for her answer.

He had seen her humbled, yet still he was not satisfied – obviously he wanted her pride ground into the dust! She lifted her head and, full of gentle dignity, confessed, 'I suspect that somehow you've guessed that I lied to you. Wendy is not my child, she's my sister. I wanted to wound your pride and that was the only way I knew how ... I'm sorry ...'

'And so you ought to be, my little tormentor!' he ground savagely, then he took her chin between his fingers and forced her to meet his heady, blazing glance full on. 'Oh, *querida*,' he groaned, 'you punished me well – no one could be devil enough to warrant the torture you piled upon my head! But I forgive you, I have to forgive you because, *mi vida*, without you I cannot live!'

He took her lips, still parted with surprise, drinking in their sweetness like a man deprived, straining her against him with such longing her bones felt crushed to pulp, yet she made no demur, the wonder of it was so great it was impossible to believe.

'I adore you, my gentle, serene little wife,' he bedevilled her. 'You drive me mad with desire, so much so that I have to ride the range for best part of the night lest my hunger should drive me into stealing once again what you would never willingly give. Oh, my heart,' one by one he kissed the tears from her cheeks, 'can *you* forgive *me* for forcing my brutal attentions upon a *virgin* child – the memory of that shameful night will haunt me for the rest of my life?'

So that was when he had discovered her secret! How foolish of her to think him incapable of realizing when he held a complete and utter novice in his arms! She clung to him, afraid to let him go in case these wonderful moments should turn out to be a mirage.

'Why,' she condemned, burying her flushed cheeks against his chest, 'did you find it necessary to torture me into admitting what you had already discovered for yourself?'

He took his time in replying, first kissing her eyes, the tip of her nose, the tiny dimple at the corner of her mouth. 'Because it is essential that we should start being honest with one another.'

Greatly daring, still unsure, and timid of arousing his flashpoint anger, she resurrected a subject that had caused her much pain.

'You demand honesty from me, so I must be entitled to the same return. Tell me,' she husked, 'am I to continue sharing you with Gabriela? Will you keep a separate compartment in your heart for her and one for me?'

'Gabriela?' Like a fly from the hide of a steer she

was brushed aside. 'There have been many Gabrielas in my life, shadows that flickered upon a wall, but only one divine substance, *mi vida,* only you are the cool candle that will cherish for ever the flame of my adoration.'

Deeply moved, Serena found the confidence to tease, 'Would it have mattered so much if Wendy really had been my child?'

This time she prodded a slumbering devil.

'*Yes!*' he rasped, his grip tightening to the point of agony. '*It would have mattered like hell!*'

An interlude followed during which he would allow no time for further words. He seemed intent upon apologizing with a kiss for everything he had done or said, every scathing remark, every hurtful action — and there had been many. So many, in fact, that passion became impatient and the fire of desire flared, devoured, and eventually absolved him of his remaining sins.

Much later they stood together by the window clasped in each other's arms watching a huge golden disc of moon shining down upon his inheritance, upon the miles of pampas, the village that housed the *huasos* and their families, the sprawling hacienda set within a maze of tropical garden. Serena sighed, and their communion was such that Juan knew immediately the thoughts that disturbed her.

'I will give it all up, if you wish,' he told her with such simple sincerity she felt ashamed of her lingering doubts. 'In fact,' his grasp tightened as she snuggled closer, 'I would enjoy the challenge of starting out afresh to provide with my own two hands the necessities of life for my small family.'

She stirred, then dared to whisper, 'You don't resent Wendy?'

He was too full of contentment to feel anger. 'I adore the *bella niña* as much as I will adore our own beautiful children. But you have not answered my question, *querida*. Grandfather has not yet left the hacienda, he was too worried about you. Shall I go to him and explain that I wish to tear up the papers we signed yesterday, as proof of my love?'

He took her sweetly troubled face between his hands and waited. He, the most arrogant of the Valdivias, was allowing her to choose his destiny, placing his life, his future and his happiness in her hands.

Serena did not hesitate. 'No,' she told him softly, 'such a decision would break your grandfather's heart. Besides,' her breath caught as his hand sought and cupped her racing heart, 'the condor needs space in which to stretch his wings. Fly swift and fly high, if you must, my love, but let us build our nest here, in our very own valley of Paradise.'

that's Entertainment!

Harlequin

the unique monthly magazine packed with good things for Harlequin readers!

A Complete Harlequin Novel

You'll get hours of reading enjoyment from Harlequin fiction. Along with a variety of specially selected short stories, every issue of the magazine contains a complete romantic novel.

Readers' Page

A lively forum for exchanging news and views from Harlequin readers. If you would like to share your thoughts, we'd love to hear from you.

Arts and Crafts

Unusual handicraft articles are a fascinating feature of Harlequin magazine. You'll enjoy making your own gifts or just being creative when you use these always clear and easy-to-follow instructions.

Author's Own Story . . .

Now, meet the very real people who create the romantic world of Harlequin! In these unusual author profiles a well-known author tells you her own personal story.

Harlequin Cookery

Temptingly delicious dishes, plain and fancy, from all over the world. Recreate these dishes from tested, detailed recipes, for your family and friends.

Faraway Places . . .

Whether it's to remind you of places you've enjoyed visiting, or to learn about places you're still hoping to see — you'll find the travel articles informative and interesting. And just perfect for armchair travelling.

Harlequin

An annual subscription to the magazine — 12 issues — costs just $9.00.
Look for the order form on the next page.